*Operational Calculus
and Generalized Functions*

Athena Series

SELECTED TOPICS IN MATHEMATICS

Edwin Hewitt, *Editor*

Arthur Erdélyi

California Institute of Technology

Operational Calculus
and Generalized Functions

HOLT, RINEHART AND WINSTON

NEW YORK

Preface

This book is based on a course offered at the California Institute of Technology. Typically, the majority of the students are advanced undergraduates (juniors and seniors), the others being beginning graduate students (mostly engineering). With a class having a firm grasp of advanced calculus, it has been found possible to cover the material, with some omissions in the last two chapters, in a one-quarter course meeting three times a week. Without omissions, and at a somewhat more leisurely pace, the material presented in the book should be sufficient for a one-semester course.

I should like to express my gratitude to Professor H. S. Zuckerman of the University of Washington who read drafts of Chapters 2 and 3 and whose comments and advice on these chapters and on the general plan of the book proved very valuable. I should also like to thank my students whose active participation in the course helped to shape it; to Professor J. C. Jaeger and the Oxford University Press for permission to use material from *Operational Methods in Applied Mathematics* by H. S. Carslaw and J. C. Jaeger; and to the secretarial staff of the Mathematics Department of the California Institute of Technology who prepared two mimeographed editions of these lecture notes as well as the typescript for this book. Finally, I should like to acknowledge publicly my sense of indebtedness to Professor Jan Mikusiński, the creator of the theory of operational calculus presented in these pages.

A. E.

Pasadena, California
November, 1961

v

Contents

vii

[1]

Introduction

1.1 Preliminary Remarks

In Heaviside's operational calculus, in particular in the application of this operational calculus to partial differential equations, difficulties arise as a result of the occurrence of certain operators whose meaning is not at all obvious. The interpretation of such operators as given by Heaviside and his successors is difficult to justify, and the range of validity of the calculus so developed remains unclear. A similar lack of clarity with regard to the range of validity also arises in connection with the use of the delta function and other impulse functions both in operational calculus and in other branches of applied mathematics.

In view of this situation one can either use operational calculus and impulse functions as a kind of shorthand or heuristic means for obtaining tentative solutions to be verified, if necessary, by the techniques of classical analysis (such an attitude seems to have been envisaged originally by Dirac when he introduced the delta function); or else it becomes necessary to develop a mathematical theory that will justify the process.

In this book such a theory will be developed—namely, the theory of *convolution quotients* due to the Polish mathematician Jan Mikusiński. This theory is based on an extension of the concept "function," an extension somewhat akin to the extension of the concept "number" from integers to rational numbers (fractions). The resulting abstract entities of Mikusiński's theory may be interpreted either as operators or as generalized functions, and they include the operators of differentiation, integration, and related operators, and also the delta function and other impulse functions. Functions (in the ordinary sense of the word) and numbers also find their places in the system of convolution quotients.

Mikusiński's theory provides a satisfactory basis for operational calculus, and it can be applied successfully to ordinary and partial differential equations with constant coefficients, difference equations, integral equations, and also in some other fields.

In sections 1.2 to 1.4 some problems are reviewed that arise in connection with operational calculus and impulse functions and some of the solutions that have been proposed are briefly indicated, including a preview of Mikusiński's theory. These sections are not required for the understanding of what follows and may be omitted. Section 1.5 includes comments on the notion of integral to be used in this book: readers possessing an adequate knowledge of integration

1

theory may omit this discussion. Some of the notations and conventions that are used in the sequel are explained in section 1.6.

Chapters 2 and 3 contain the elementary theory of convolution quotients and its application to ordinary linear differential equations with constant coefficients and to certain integral equations. These two chapters form a self-contained whole, and a short course may be based on them. In chapter 4 the convergence theory of convolution quotients is developed and operator functions are introduced; and in chapter 5 differential equations involving operator functions are discussed and exponential functions of operators are introduced. The tools developed in these chapters are then applied in chapters 6 and 7 to problems in partial differential equations.

1.2 Heaviside Calculus; Laplace Transforms

In some contexts—for instance, for the solution of ordinary linear differential equations with constant coefficients—it is usual to treat the operator of differentiation as an algebraic entity. The differential equation

$$a_0 \frac{d^n z}{dt^n} + a_1 \frac{d^{n-1}z}{dt^{n-1}} + \cdots + a_{n-1} \frac{dz}{dt} + a_n z = f(t) \tag{1}$$

is written in the form $P(D) z = f$, where $D = d/dt$, and

$$P(D) = a_0 D^n + a_1 D^{n-1} + \cdots + a_{n-1}D + a_n \tag{2}$$

is a polynomial with constant coefficients. The solution of (1) appears as

$$z = \frac{1}{P(D)} f, \tag{3}$$

and this solution is then evaluated by factorizing $P(D)$, decomposing $[P(D)]^{-1}$ in partial fractions, and interpreting each term separately. This "symbolic method" can be fully justified by elementary means and is presented in many textbooks on differential equations. [See, for instance, Agnew (1960) Chapter 6.]

Heaviside developed the application of similar techniques to partial differential equations. In general, the operators arising here are transcendental functions of D, and it is difficult to develop, and even more difficult to justify, a correct interpretation of the resulting operational expressions.

As an example, let us consider the following boundary value problem for $z = z(x, t)$ (subscripts denote partial differentiation):

$$z_{xx} = z_t \quad \text{for} \quad x, t > 0; \qquad z(0, t) = f(t); \qquad z(x, t) \to 0 \quad \text{as} \quad x \to \infty. \tag{4}$$

With $D = d/dt$, the partial differential equation becomes $z_{xx} = Dz$, and its general solution,

$$z = A \exp(xD^{1/2}) + B \exp(-xD^{1/2}). \tag{5}$$

From $z \to 0$ as $x \to \infty$, Heaviside would conclude that $A = 0$ and from $z(0, t) = f(t)$, $B = f(t)$. The operational solution of (4) is then

$$z = \exp\left(-xD^{1/2}\right) f(t). \tag{6}$$

It is difficult to justify this process (especially the conclusion that $A = 0$), or to interpret (6). Moreover, it is strange that no initial condition was used in obtaining this solution. (It turns out that Heaviside's solution vanishes at $t = 0$).

It appears difficult to base a mathematical theory of this process on the operator $D = d/dt$, and attempts to use the inverse operator (integration from 0 to t) instead were only partially successful. For this reason Dalton (1954) uses as primary operator the operator ω_λ defined by

$$\omega_\lambda f(t) = f(t) + \lambda \int_0^t e^{\lambda(t-\theta)} f(\theta)\, d\theta$$

which operates on arbitrary integrable functions and is shown to possess an inverse, given by

$$\omega_\lambda^{-1} g(t) = g(t) - \lambda \int_0^t g(\theta)\, d\theta$$

for arbitrary integrable functions. Dalton's theory is probably the best available justification of Heaviside's calculus by means that are akin to Heaviside's own tools.

The most widely used mathematical theory of operational calculus is based on the *Laplace transformation.* This is a functional transformation changing the function $f(t)$ of the nonnegative real variable t into the function

$$L[f; s] = \int_0^\infty e^{-st} f(t)\, dt \tag{7}$$

which turns out to be an analytic function of the complex variable s. By integration by parts,

$$\int_0^\infty e^{-st} f'(t)\, dt = -f(0) + s \int_0^\infty e^{-st} f(t)\, dt$$

or

$$L[f'] = s\, L[f] - f(0), \tag{8}$$

and this relation is the clue to the connection of Laplace transforms with operational calculus. At any rate, for functions that vanish at $t = 0$, differentiation of f corresponds to multiplication of the Laplace transform by s. The complex variable s takes the place of the operator D, and initial conditions can be accounted for.

Let us solve the boundary value problem (4) by this technique, setting $L[z; s] = Z(x, s)$ and using (8) to obtain

$$Z_{xx} = sZ - z(x, 0); \qquad Z(0, s) = F(s) = L[f]; \qquad Z \to 0 \quad \text{as} \quad x \to \infty.$$

Assuming $z(x, 0) = 0$, we obtain virtually Heaviside's problem and its general solution

$$Z(x, s) = A \exp(x \sqrt{s}) + B \exp(-x \sqrt{s}).$$

Restricting s to the complex plane cut along the negative real axis, we take $\mathrm{Re} \sqrt{s} > 0$. From the boundary conditions we have $A = 0$, $B = F(s)$, and corresponding to (6),

$$Z(x, s) = F(s) \exp(-x \sqrt{s}),$$

and thus

$$\int_0^\infty e^{-st} z(x, t)\, dt = F(s) \exp(-x \sqrt{s}). \tag{9}$$

The solution of this integral equation is also the solution of our boundary value problem. Now (9) is Laplace's integral equation for the solution of which several methods are known.

This derivation of (9) involves several steps needing justification, such as differentiation with respect to x under the integral sign; but these are difficulties that can be analyzed in the light of known theorems in advanced calculus.

The Laplace transform theory of operational calculus is presented at varying degrees of mathematical sophistication in numerous books by Churchill (1958); Doetsch; Gardner and Barnes; McLachlan; Widder; and others. In the book by van der Pol and Bremmer (1950), the theory is based on the two-sided Laplace transform

$$\int_{-\infty}^\infty e^{-st} f(t)\, dt.$$

Laplace transform theory is precise and rigorous, and it requires no tools other than those of classical analysis. Nevertheless, especially lately, other theories have been gaining ground. The protagonists of these contend that Laplace transforms are foreign to the nature of operational calculus, that their use needlessly and unnaturally restricts the functions that the theory is able to handle (excluding, for instance, $\exp t^2$), and that this theory (like Dalton's) fails to account for the delta function and other impulse functions.

1.3 The Delta Function

In mathematical physics one often encounters "impulsive" forces acting for a short time only. A unit impulse can be described by a function $p(t)$ which vanishes outside of a short interval and satisfies $\int_{-\infty}^\infty p(t)\, dt = 1$. It is convenient to idealize such forces as "instantaneous" and to attempt to describe them by a function, $\delta(t)$, which vanishes except for a single value of t, which we take as

$t = 0$, is undefined at $t = 0$, and satisfies $\int_{-\infty}^{\infty} \delta(t)\, dt = 1$. Such a function should possess the "sifting property"

$$\int_{-\infty}^{\infty} \delta(u)\, f(u)\, du = f(0) \tag{1}$$

for every continuous function f.

Such, and similar other, "impulse functions" are being used successfully in applied mathematics and mathematical physics, even though it can be proved that no function (in the sense of the mathematical definition of this term) can possibly possess the sifting property. As in the case of operational calculus, the use of impulse functions can either be defended as a shorthand, or else justified by a mathematical theory. There is no shortage of such theories.

The delta function being an idealization of functions vanishing outside of a short interval, it seems natural to try and approximate the delta function by such functions. If $p(t)$ satisfies (i) $\int_{-\infty}^{\infty} p(t)\, dt = 1$ and (ii) $p(t) = 0$ outside the interval $(-1, 1)$, then the function $p_n(t) = np(nt)$ satisfies (i) and vanishes outside $(-1/n, 1/n)$, and it may be regarded as an ever improving approximation to the delta function as $n \to \infty$. Indeed,

$$\lim_{n \to \infty} \int_{-\infty}^{\infty} p_n(u)\, f(u)\, du = f(0) \tag{2}$$

can be proved for all continuous functions f. It may be remarked that we clearly have

$$\lim_{n \to \infty} \int_{-\infty}^{t} p_n(u)\, du = \begin{array}{ll} 0 & \text{if} \quad t < 0 \\ 1 & \text{if} \quad t > 0 \end{array},$$

thus showing that in some sense the delta function may be considered as the derivative of Heaviside's unit function H defined by

$$H(t) = \begin{array}{ll} 0 & t < 0 \\ 1 & t \geq 0 \end{array} \tag{3}$$

A rather different kind of theory attempts to define the delta function by its action on continuous functions, this action being described by the sifting property. In this theory, any analytical operation that, acting on a continuous function f, produces $f(0)$ is a representation of the delta function. Such an analytical operation can be constructed in terms of a Stieltjes integral since

$$\int_{-\infty}^{\infty} f(u)\, dH(u) = f(0)$$

for all continuous functions f. If H were absolutely continuous, we should have

$$\int f(u)\, dH(u) = \int f(u)\, H'(u)\, du$$

so that here too the delta function appears as the derivative, in some sense, of the unit function.

For the history and theories of the delta function see for instance van der Pol and Bremmer (1950).

Such theories are adequate, and it is possible to develop theories of this kind for each impulse function one encounters. Nevertheless, it seems desirable to develop one single general theory that embraces all impulse (and other "improper") functions currently used and preferably also those that may be expected to arise in future work. Somewhat suprisingly, such a general theory seems to necessitate a radical departure from some of the basic concepts of classical analysis.

One such general theory, initiated recently by Schmieden and Laugwitz (1958), is based on an extension of the concept of real numbers. In the number system introduced by these authors there are infinitely small and infinitely large numbers, and in this system the delta function becomes a function (its value at $t = 0$ being infinitely large). Other theories are based on an extension of the concept "function."

PROBLEMS

1. Show that

$$\int_{-\infty}^{\infty} \delta(u) f(t - u) \, du = f(t)$$

for continuous functions f.

2. Define the "sifting property" appropriate to derivatives of the delta function.

3. Show that each of the following sequences of functions approaches the delta function, in the sense of (2), as $n \to \infty$.

(i) $\quad p_n(t) = \begin{cases} 0 & \text{if} \quad t \geq \dfrac{1}{n} \quad \text{or} \quad t \leq -\dfrac{1}{n} \\[2ex] \dfrac{n}{2} & \text{if} \quad -\dfrac{1}{n} < t < \dfrac{1}{n} \end{cases}$

(ii) $\quad p_n(t) = \dfrac{n}{2} e^{-n|t|}$

(iii) $\quad p_n(t) = \dfrac{1}{\pi} \dfrac{n}{1 + n^2 t^2}$

(iv) $\quad p_n(t) = n\pi^{-1/2} \exp(-n^2 t^2)$.

1.4 Generalized Functions

There are several extensions and generalizations of the concept of a mathematical function. Here we slall discuss two of these generalizations which have proved useful in applied mathematics.

First we shall briefly indicate the theory of *distributions* as developed by Schwartz (1950, 1951) [see also Halperin (1952)].

We call infinitely differentiable functions of t defined for $-\infty < t < \infty$ and vanishing outside some finite interval (which may vary from function to function), *testing functions*, and denote by $\mathfrak{D}$ the set of all testing functions. We define convergence in $\mathfrak{D}$ by saying that $\phi_n \to \phi$ as $n \to \infty$ if each ϕ_n is a testing function, all ϕ_n vanish outside some finite interval that is independent of n, and each derivative of the ϕ_n converges uniformly to the corresponding derivative of ϕ. For continuous functions f, the infinite integral in

$$f\langle\phi\rangle = \int_{-\infty}^{\infty} f(t)\,\phi(t)\,dt \tag{1}$$

converges for each ϕ in $\mathfrak{D}$, and defines an "evaluation" of f on elements of $\mathfrak{D}$. In classical analysis we think of a function f as characterized by its values $f(t)$; we can now characterize a function by its evaluations on all testing functions (It can be proved that two continuous functions possessing the same evaluation on each testing function are identical in the sense of also possessing the same values for all real t.)

For a fixed f, (1) assigns a real or complex number to every element of $\mathfrak{D}$, and thus defines a *functional* on $\mathfrak{D}$. This functional is linear, $f\langle a\phi + b\theta\rangle = a\,f\langle\phi\rangle + b\,f\langle\theta\rangle$ for any two real or complex numbers a and b, and any two testing functions ϕ and θ; and it is *continuous*, $f\langle\phi_n\rangle \to f\langle\phi\rangle$ in the sense of convergence of numbers provided that $\phi_n \to \phi$ in the sense of convergence in $\mathfrak{D}$. Thus every continuous function (as a matter of fact, every locally integrable function) defines a continuous linear functional on $\mathfrak{D}$. Not all continuous linear functionals on $\mathfrak{D}$ originate in this manner. For instance,

$$\delta\langle\phi\rangle = \phi(0)$$

defines a continuous linear functional on $\mathfrak{D}$, and this functional cannot be generated by a locally integrable function—indeed, it corresponds to the delta function.

We now propose to call continuous linear functionals on $\mathfrak{D}$ *distributions*, and regard distributions as generalized functions. Distributions are abstract entities that possess some, but clearly not all, properties traditionally associated with functions; in particular, they do not in general have "values" at specified values of t. Nevertheless, distributions have been successfully used in Fourier analysis, in connection with ordinary and partial differential equations, and integral equations, and they account satisfactorily for all improper functions arising in such investigations. Corresponding generalized functions have been defined for the case of several independent variables and in some more general situations.

There are at least two alternative approaches to the theory of distributions. One of these represents distributions as generalized limits of functions [see, for instance, Temple (1953), Korevaar (1955), Lighthill (1958)] and the other, as generalized derivatives of functions [see, for instance, Sauer (1958)]. These approaches will not be presented here; the reader will have no difficulty in seeing that the various theories of distributions correspond closely to the various theories of the delta function indicated in Section 1.3.

We now turn to an entirely different concept of generalized functions, to Mikusiński's *convolution quotients*. This concept is less general than that of distributions in that it is not designed to cope with functions of unrestricted real variables. It is most successful in its application to functions of a single nonnegative variable, although it has been extended to functions of several nonnegative variables, and to functions of a real variable ranging over a finite interval.

Let us start with the set $\mathfrak{C}$ of all continuous functions f of a nonnegative variable t, and define the *convolution fg* of two such functions f and g, by the equation

$$fg(t) = \int_0^t f(u)\, g(t - u)\, du \qquad\qquad t \geq 0. \qquad (2)$$

The operation of convolution has the character of a multiplication. The sifting property of the delta function can be expressed in convolution notation as $\delta g = g$ for all g in $\mathfrak{C}$ so that the delta function acts as a unit element for this multiplication. We now introduce *convolution quotients f/g* very much in the same way as rational numbers are introduced as quotients of integers. Convolution quotients can be defined in terms of continuous functions by means of ordered pairs, (f, g), for which appropriate operations are introduced. Just as some rational fractions can be identified with integers, so also some convolution quotients can be identified with continuous functions, others with discontinuous integrable functions, yet others with real or complex numbers. The convolution quotient (g, g) corresponds to the delta function, and there are convolution quotients corresponding to other impulse functions. It turns out that operators of differentiation and integration can also be indentified with certain convolution quotients, and the resulting theory leads to elegant methods for solving ordinary linear differential equations with constant coefficients, and certain integral equations.

Next, operator functions—that is, convolution quotients depending on parameters—are considered. Convergence of a sequence of convolution quotients and continuity and differentiability of operator functions depending on a continuously varying parameter are introduced, and thus the tools are created for a successful application of convolution quotients to partial differential equations.

The program thus outlined will be carried out in this book. For other aspects of the theory of convolution quotients the reader may be referred to Mikusiński's original papers (some of which are listed at the end of this book) and to the English translation of his textbook [Mikusiński (1959)]. It may be noted here that an alternative theory of convolution quotients was proposed by J. D. Weston (1957, 1959 a, b) who proceeds via a generalization of the Laplace transformation.

1.5 Integration

Integration will enter into our work in many important ways. In particular, convolution integrals

$$h(x) = \int_0^x f(x - y)\, g(y)\, dy \tag{1}$$

will be basic for the whole theory, and the fundamental theorem of integral calculus,

$$\int_a^b f'(x)\, dx = f(b) - f(a), \tag{2}$$

will turn out to be the clue to the interpretation of differential operators.

Certain results on (1) and (2) can be formulated most concisely within the framework of Lebesgue's theory of integration. For any two locally integrable functions f and g, (1) defines $h(x)$ almost everywhere, the function thus defined being locally integrable; and (2) holds whenever f is absolutely continuous. Readers acquainted with the Lebesgue theory of integration should have no difficulty in reformulating some of the later results and proofs in the language of that theory; for the sake of other readers a more elementary approach has been adopted in the text.

Clearly, $h(x)$ exists and is a continuous function of x if f and g are continuous, and (2) certainly holds if f is continuously differentiable; but already the example of Heaviside's unit function illustrates the appearance of discontinuous functions in our considerations, and functions with infinite discontinuities, such as $|x - 1|^{-1/2}$, also frequently occur in applied mathematics. Thus, a rigid restriction to continuous functions seems inappropriate, and we shall allow our integrands to have discontinuities, provided only that the integrals exist as finite sums of proper Riemann integrals or absolutely convergent improper Riemann integrals.

In the sequel we shall consider an interval I which may be finite or infinite, open, closed, or half-open; and we shall say that a subset S of I consists of *isolated points* if the points of S have no limit point in I. In this case each closed finite subinterval of I will contain at most a finite number of points of S.

DEFINITION: A function f is said to be *locally integrable* on I if (i) $f(x)$ is defined on I with the possible exception of a set S_f of isolated points of I called the *singularities* of f; (ii) f is continuous in I except at its singularities; and (iii) the integral of f over any closed subinterval of I containing no singularity of f in its interior exists either as a proper Riemann integral, or else as an absolutely convergent improper Riemann integral.

Let f be locally integrable in I, and let $[\alpha, \beta]$ be a closed subinterval of I. Suppose $c_1 < c_2 < \cdots < c_{n-1}$ are the singularities of f in the open interval (α, β), and set $c_0 = \alpha$, $c_n = \beta$ (these may also be singularities). Then for each $k = 0, 1, \cdots, n - 1$, the integral

$$\int_{c_k}^{c_{k+1}} f(x) \, dx$$

exists either as a proper Riemann integral or else as an absolutely convergent improper Riemann integral. We define

$$\int_{\alpha}^{\beta} f(x) \, dx = \sum_{k=0}^{n-1} \int_{c_k}^{c_{k+1}} f(x) \, dx,$$

and say that f is *absolutely integrable* on the closed interval $[\alpha, \beta]$.

If I itself is a bounded closed interval, then a function which is locally integrable on I is also absolutely integrable there but in the case of an infinite or not closed interval I, this need not be the case.

Condition (ii) of the above definition may be replaced by the less restrictive condition: (ii') f is properly Riemann integrable over any closed subinterval of I containing no singularity of f; but we shall not make use of this generalization here.

The results on (1) and (2) which will be used in our presentation of operational calculus can then be summarized in the following two theorems.

THEOREM A: If f is continuous in I and differentiable except on a set of isolated points, and if f' is locally integrable on I, then (2) holds for all a and b in I.

A function satisfying the conditions of this theorem will be said to possess a locally integrable derivative.

THEOREM B: If f and g are locally integrable on the semi-infinite interval $x \geq 0$, then the integral (1) exists for $x \geq 0$ except possibly on a set of isolated points, and defines a function $h(x)$ which is itself locally integrable on $x \geq 0$.

The proof of theorem A is very simple. Let $c_1 < c_2 < \cdots < c_{n-1}$ be the singularities of f' in $a < x < b$, and set $c_0 = a$, $c_n = b$. For a fixed k, $k = 0, 1, \cdots, n - 1$, let $c_k < \alpha < \beta < c_{k+1}$. Since f is continuously differentiable for $\alpha \leq x \leq \beta$, we have

$$\int_{\alpha}^{\beta} f'(x) \, dx = f(\beta) - f(\alpha).$$

As $\alpha \to c_k$ and $\beta \to c_{k+1}$, the right-hand side approaches $f(c_{k+1}) - f(c_k)$ since f is continuous, and the left-hand side approaches the (possibly improper) integral

$$\int_{c_k}^{c_{k+1}} f'(x)\, dx$$

whose existence is a consequence of the local integrability of f'. Thus,

$$\int_{c_k}^{c_{k+1}} f'(x)\, dx = f(c_{k+1}) - f(c_k) \qquad k = 0, 1, \cdots, n-1,$$

and we obtain (2) by adding these relations.

A detailed proof of theorem B is somewhat more involved, and we shall content ourselves with an outline of the proof omitting some of the details.

Let S_f and S_g be the sets of singularities of f and g, and let S_h be the set of those values of x for which $f(x-y)g(y)$ fails to be absolutely integrable for $0 \leq y \leq x$. This latter circumstance can arise only if for some y in S_g we have $x - y$ in S_f: thus, S_h is a set of isolated points. If a fixed x_0 is not in S_h, then $f(x-y)g(y)$ is an absolutely integrable function of y for $0 < y < x$ not only for $x = x_0$ but also in some neighborhood of x_0. We wish to show that $h(x)$ is continuous at x_0 so that condition (ii) of the definition of locally integrable functions holds.

If the interval $\alpha \leq y \leq \beta$ contains no point for which y is in S_g or $x - y$ is in S_f, then the integrand of

$$\int_{\alpha}^{\beta} f(x-y)g(y)\, dy \tag{3}$$

is a continuous function of x and y, and the integral itself is clearly a continuous function of x. Thus, any possible discontinuities of $h(x)$ must arise from the contribution of those parts of the integral for which y is in S_g or else $x - y$ is in S_f.

Let x_0 be fixed, x_0 not in S_h, and let c be in S_g, $0 < c < x_0$. Then there exists a positive number δ so that f is continuous, and hence uniformly continuous, in the closed interval $[x_0 - c - 2\delta, x_0 - c + 2\delta]$. Consider the integral

$$F(x) = \int_{c-\delta}^{c+\delta} f(x-y)g(y)\, dy \qquad x_0 - \delta \leq x \leq x_0 + \delta \tag{4}$$

in which the first factor of the integrand is continuous, and the second factor is absolutely integrable. We have

$$F(x) - F(x_0) = \int_{c-\delta}^{c+\delta} [f(x-y) - f(x_0-y)]g(y)\, dy,$$

and the continuity of F at x_0 follows from the uniform continuity of f.

The argument for the integral

$$\int_{x-c-\delta}^{x-c+\delta} f(x-y)g(y)\,dy \tag{5}$$

with c in S_f is similar; indeed (5) can be reduced to (4) by a change of the variable of integration from y to $z = x - y$.

Since (1) is the sum of a finite number of integrals of the forms (3), (4), (5), it follows that h is continuous at x_0.

We now know that h is continuous, except possibly at points of S_h, and wish to verify that condition (iii) of our definition is also satisfied. Let $0 \le \alpha \le x \le \beta$ be a closed interval containing no point of S_h in its interior, and let $\alpha < a < b < \beta$. Since $h(x)$ is continuous for $a \le x \le b$, the integral

$$\int_a^b h(x)\,dx = \int_a^b \left[\int_0^x f(x-y)g(y)\,dy \right] dx$$

exists. Moreover, it can be proved [for instance by a decomposition of the inner integral into its constituent parts of the forms (3), (4), (5)] that the order of integrations may be interchanged so that

$$\int_a^b h(x)\,dx = \int_0^b g(y) \left[\int_{\max(a,y)}^b f(x-y)\,dx \right] dy.$$

We now have the following estimates

$$\int_a^b |h(x)|\,dx \le \int_0^b |g(y)| \left[\int_y^b |f(x-y)|\,dx \right] dy \le \int_0^b |g(y)|\,dy \int_0^b |f(z)|\,dz$$

and hence

$$\int_a^b |h(x)|\,dx \le \int_0^\beta |g(y)|\,dy \int_0^\beta |f(z)|\,dz.$$

As a decreases to α and b increases to β, the left-hand side increases: since it is bounded by the right-hand side, it approaches a limit, thus showing that the integral

$$\int_\alpha^\beta h(x)\,dx$$

exists, at worst as an absolutely convergent improper Riemann integral. Theorem B is now established.

1.6 Notations and Conventions

We shall be concerned mainly with real or complex valued functions of a nonnegative real variable t. A typical notation for such a function will be f or $\{f(t)\}$, denoting the function as a whole entity (envisaged as the graph of the function or else as a mapping of the semi-infinite interval $t \geq 0$ into the complex plane), while $f(t)$ will denote the value of the function at the point t: this value is a (real or complex) number. This convention refers to functions of t and will be observed throughout the book. Eventually we shall also consider functions of other variables. We shall write ϕ or $\phi(x)$ for a numerical valued function of x and will often write $f(x) = \{f(x, t)\}$ if we wish to indicate that we envisage, for each fixed x, $f(x)$ as a function of t.

A new symbol (term) occurring in a formula (statement) is to be understood as being defined by that formula or statement. References are given as follows: 2.3 refers to section 2.3; (1) refers to equation (1) of the section in which the reference occurs; and 2.3(1) refers to equation (1) of section 2.3. References to the literature are given at the end of the book and are quoted by giving the name of the author and the year of publication; thus, Mikusiński (1959) refers to the English translation of Mikusiński's *Operational Calculus*.

A list of special symbols appears at the end of the book.

[2]

The Algebra of Convolution Quotients

2.1 The Convolution Ring

DEFINITION 1. (i) $\mathfrak{N}$ is the field of complex numbers. (ii) t is a nonnegative real variable. (iii) $\mathfrak{C}$ is the class of (real- or complex-valued) continuous functions of a nonnegative real variable.

DEFINITION* 2. For $\alpha \epsilon \mathfrak{N}$ and a, $b \epsilon \mathfrak{C}$ let (i) $a + b$ be the function whose value at t is $a(t) + b(t)$; (ii) αa be the function whose value at t is $\alpha a(t)$; and (iii) ab be the function whose value at t is

$$ab(t) = \int_0^t a(u)\, b(t - u)\, du. \tag{1}$$

ab is called the *convolution* (or resultant, composition, Faltung) of a and b. ff will be denoted by f^2, and a similar notation will be employed for higher convolution powers.

Throughout this book, h will denote the constant function $\{1\}$ which is the restriction of Heaviside's unit function to the half-line $t \geq 0$. We have

$$h(t) = 1$$

$$h^2(t) = \int_0^t h(u)\, h(t - u)\, du = t$$

$$h^3(t) = \int_0^t h^2(u)\, h(t - u)\, du = \frac{t^2}{2}$$

and it is easy to prove by induction that

$$h^n = \left\{ \frac{t^{n-1}}{(n - 1)!} \right\} \qquad n = 1, 2, 3, \cdots. \tag{2}$$

More generally, we define (tentatively at this stage; see section 4.3 example 2)

$$h^\alpha = \left\{ \frac{t^{\alpha-1}}{\Gamma(\alpha)} \right\} \qquad \operatorname{Re} \alpha > 0, \tag{3}$$

---

* ϵ stands for "in" or "a member of." Thus, $a \epsilon \mathfrak{N}$ means that a is a complex number.

where $\Gamma(\alpha)$ denotes the gamma function, and note that

$$\int_0^t (t-u)^{\alpha-1}\, u^{\beta-1}\, du = \frac{\Gamma(\alpha)\,\Gamma(\beta)}{\Gamma(\alpha+\beta)}\, t^{\alpha+\beta-1} \qquad \mathrm{Re}\ \alpha > 0,\ \mathrm{Re}\ \beta > 0,$$

and consequently

$$h^\alpha h^\beta = h^{\alpha+\beta} \qquad\qquad \mathrm{Re}\ \alpha > 0,\ \mathrm{Re}\ \beta > 0, \qquad (4)$$

by Euler's integral of the first kind. The definition (3) is motivated by the circumstance that it reduces to (2) when α is a positive integer, and obeys the index law (4).

Clearly, $h \in \mathfrak{C}$. For any $f \in \mathfrak{C}$ we have $hf = \{\int_0^t f(u)\, du\}$ so that convolution of a (continuous) function with h effects an integration of that function with 0 as a fixed lower limit. In this sense, h may be regarded as the *operator of integration* and similarly h^n, as the operator of n times repeated integration. We shall also regard h^α as the operator of *integration of fractional order* α; indeed $h^\alpha f$ is the Riemann-Liouville integral of order α of f.

The algebraic properties of the operations introduced in definition 2 are summarized in

THEOREM 1. For $\alpha,\ \beta \in \mathfrak{R}$ and $a,\ b,\ c \in \mathfrak{C}$ we have

(i) $a+b,\quad \alpha a,\quad ab \in \mathfrak{C}$;

(ii) $a+b = b+a,\quad a+(b+c) = (a+b)+c$;

(iii) $\alpha(a+b) = \alpha a + \alpha b,\quad (\alpha+\beta)a = \alpha a + \beta a,$
$\alpha(ab) = (\alpha a)b = a(\alpha b),\quad (\alpha\beta)a = \alpha(\beta a)$;

(iv) $ab = ba,\quad a(bc) = (ab)c,\quad (a+b)c = ac + bc.$

The proofs of (i), (ii), (iii), and of the last part of (iv) are left to the reader. To prove the first part of (iv), we set $u = t - v$ to obtain

$$ab(t) = \int_0^t a(u)\, b(t-u)\, du = \int_0^t b(v)\, a(t-v)\, dv = ba(t),$$

and to prove the second part of (iv) we interchange the order of integrations to obtain

$$a(bc)\,(t) = \int_0^t a(u)\left[\int_0^{t-u} b(t-u-v)\, c(v)\, dv\right] du$$

$$= \int_0^t \left[\int_0^{t-v} a(u)\, b(t-v-u)\, du\right] c(v)\, dv = (ab)\, c(t).$$

(i) shows that $\mathfrak{C}$ is closed under the (algebraic) operations of addition, multiplication by a scalar (number), and convolution. (ii) and (iii) show that $\mathfrak{C}$ is a *vector space* over the field of complex numbers. The null element of this vector space is the function $\{0\}$. The vector space is infinite dimensional, since the functions h^n, $n = 1, 2, 3, \cdots$ are linearly independent. (ii) and (iv) show that $\mathfrak{C}$ is also a *commutative ring* which we shall call the *convolution ring*. The zero element of this ring is again the function $\{0\}$. There is no unit element in the convolution ring, for a unit element e would have to satisfy $ea = a$ for every $a \in \mathfrak{C}$, in particular, $eh = h$ or $\int_0^t e(u)\,du = 1$ for all $t \geq 0$; and this is clearly impossible. Indeed, a unit element would have to show the sifting property of the delta function, and its nonexistence is a consequence of the nonexistence of the delta function as a function in the mathematical sense of the term.

We now attempt to introduce (convolution $-$) division in our ring. In order to do this, we must ask whether the solution of the equation $zb = a$ in which a and b are given continuous functions and z is an unknown continuous function, if it exists, is unique. The affirmative answer to this question is the burden of the theorem to which the next section is devoted.

PROBLEMS

1. Which of the following functions belong to $\mathfrak{C}$?

$$\{1\}, \quad \{t\}, \quad \left\{\frac{1}{t}\right\}, \quad \{\sqrt{t}\}, \quad \left\{\frac{1}{\sqrt{t}}\right\}, \quad \{t^n\}\ n \geq 0,$$

$$\left\{\frac{1}{t \pm 1}\right\}, \quad \{\sqrt{|t \pm 1|}\}, \quad \left\{\frac{1}{\sqrt{|t \pm 1|}}\right\}, \quad \left\{\frac{1}{t + \alpha}\right\}, \quad \left\{\exp\left(t \pm \frac{1}{t}\right)\right\},$$

$$\{\exp t^2\}, \quad \{\sec t\}, \quad \{\tan t\}, \quad \{\tanh t\}, \quad \{\tan^{-1} t\}.$$

2. Show that if a, b, $c \in \mathfrak{C}$ then also $a + b$, $ab \in \mathfrak{C}$ and $(a + b)c = ac + bc$ (this is part of Theorem 1).

3. n is a positive integer, $\operatorname{Re}\alpha > 0$ and $\operatorname{Re}\beta > 0$. Evaluate

(i) $\{e^t\}^n$;   (ii) $\{t^\alpha\}\{t^\beta\}$;   (iii) $\{t^\alpha\}^n$.

4. Use the properties of $\mathfrak{C}$ to simplify

(i) $\{\cos^2 t\}\{1\} + \{1\}\{\sin^2 t\}$;

(ii) $\{1 - t\}\{e^t\} + \{e^{-t}\}\{1 + t\} - \{1 - t\}\{e^{-t}\} - \{e^t\}\{1 + t\}$.

Hence or otherwise evaluate these expressions.

2.2 Divisors of Zero

THEOREM 2. The convolution ring has no divisors of zero; that is, if a, $b \in \mathfrak{C}$ and $ab = \{0\}$, then either $a = \{0\}$ or $b = \{0\}$.

This theorem is a special case of a famous theorem due to Titchmarsh. There are several proofs known, most of which use the theory of analytic or harmonic functions. The proof to be given here is elementary; it is due to Mikusiński and Ryll-Nardzewski, and it will be given in several steps. [See Mikusiński (1959).]

LEMMA 1. If $\{g(u)\}$ is continuous for $0 \le u \le T$, and $0 \le t \le T$, then

$$\sum_{k=1}^{\infty} \frac{(-1)^{k-1}}{k!} \int_0^T e^{kx(t-u)} g(u)\, du \to \int_0^t g(u)\, du \qquad \text{as} \qquad x \to \infty. \tag{1}$$

Proof. We have

$$\sum_{k=1}^{\infty} \frac{(-1)^{k-1}}{k!} e^{kx(t-u)} = 1 - \exp\left[-e^{x(t-u)}\right],$$

and for fixed x and t, the infinite series on the left converges uniformly in u for $0 \le u \le T$. Consequently, summation may be carried out under the integral sign on the left of (1), leading to

$$\int_0^T (1 - \exp\left[-e^{x(t-u)}\right]) g(u)\, du.$$

We set

$$I(x) = \int_0^T \{1 - \exp\left[-e^{x(t-u)}\right]\} g(u)\, du - \int_0^t g(u)\, du$$

and wish to prove that $I(x) \to 0$ as $x \to \infty$. For this purpose, let us set

$$I_1 = -\int_0^{t-\delta} \exp\left[-e^{x(t-u)}\right] g(u)\, du,$$

$$I_2 = -\int_{t-\delta}^{t} \exp\left[-e^{x(t-u)}\right] g(u)\, du,$$

$$I_3 = \int_t^{t+\delta'} \{1 - \exp\left[-e^{x(t-u)}\right]\} g(u)\, du,$$

$$I_4 = \int_{t+\delta'}^{T} \{1 - \exp\left[-e^{x(t-u)}\right]\} g(u)\, du,$$

where $\delta = 0$ if $t = 0$, $0 < \delta < t$ otherwise, $\delta' = 0$ if $t = T$, $0 < \delta' < T - t$ otherwise. In any event, $I(x) = I_1 + I_2 + I_3 + I_4$.

Since $\{g(u)\}$ is continuous, $|g(u)| \le M$ for some $M \ge 0$ and $0 \le u \le T$, and we have the estimates

$$|I_1| \le MT \exp(-e^{x\delta}), \qquad |I_2| \le M\delta, \qquad |I_3| \le M\delta',$$

$$|I_4| \le MT\left[1 - \exp(-e^{-x\delta'})\right].$$

Given $\epsilon > 0$, first choose δ and δ' so that $|I_2| < \epsilon/4$, $|I_3| < \epsilon/4$; and having fixed δ and δ', choose x_0 so that $|I_1| < \epsilon/4$ and $|I_4| < \epsilon/4$ for $x = x_0$. Then clearly $|I(x)| < \epsilon$ for $x > x_0$ and since ϵ was an arbitrary positive number, this proves (1).

LEMMA 2. If $\{f(t)\}$ is continuous for $0 \le t \le T$ and $\left| \int_0^T e^{nt} f(t) \, dt \right| \le M$ for $n = 1, 2, \cdots$, then $f(t) = 0$ for $0 \le t \le T$.

Proof. We have

$$\left| \sum_{k=1}^{\infty} \frac{(-1)^{k-1}}{k!} \int_0^T e^{kn(t-u)} f(T-u) \, du \right|$$

$$\le \sum_{k=1}^{\infty} \frac{1}{k!} e^{kn(t-T)} \left| \int_0^T e^{kn(T-u)} f(T-u) \, du \right|$$

$$\le M \left\{ \exp\left[e^{-n(T-t)} \right] - 1 \right\}.$$

If $t < T$, the last expression approaches zero as $n \to \infty$, and lemma 1, with $g(u) = f(T-u)$, shows that $\int_0^t f(T-u) \, du = 0$ for $0 \le t < T$. Since f is continuous, it follows that $f(t) = 0$ for $0 \le t \le T$.

LEMMA 3. (Lerch's theorem.) If $\{f(u)\}$ is continuous for $0 \le u < U$ and $\int_0^U u^n f(u) = 0$ for $n = 1, 2, \cdots$, then $f(u) = 0$ for $0 \le u \le U$.

Proof. Fix u_0, $0 < u_0 < U$. Since

$$\int_0^U \left(\frac{u}{u_0} \right)^n f(x) \, du = 0,$$

we have

$$\left| \int_{u_0}^U \left(\frac{u}{u_0} \right)^n f(u) \, du \right| = \left| - \int_0^{u_0} \left(\frac{u}{u_0} \right)^n f(u) \, du \right| \le \int_0^{u_0} |f(u)| \, du \le M u_0$$

if $|f(u)| \le M$ for $0 \le u \le U$. On the left-hand side we set $u = u_0 e^t$, $U = u_0 e^T$, $f(u_0 e^t) e^t = F(t)$ and obtain

$$\left| \int_0^T e^{nt} F(t) \, dt \right| \le M \qquad\qquad n = 1, 2, \cdots.$$

By lemma 2, $F(t) = 0$ for $0 \le t \le T$, and hence $f(u) = 0$ for $u_0 \le u \le U$. Since this holds for each u_0 between 0 and U, we have $f(u) = 0$ for $0 < u \le U$, and since f is continuous at $u = 0$, $f(u) = 0$ for $0 \le u \le U$.

LEMMA 4. If $\{f(t)\}$ is continuous and $f^2(t) = 0$, for $0 \le t \le 2T$, then $f(t) = 0$ for $0 \le t \le T$.

COROLLARY. If $f \in \mathfrak{C}$ and $f^2 = \{0\}$, then $f = \{0\}$.

Proof. Since

$$f^2(t) = \int_0^t f(u) f(t-u)\, du = 0 \qquad \text{for} \qquad 0 \le t \le 2T,$$

we have

$$\int_0^{2T} e^{n(2T-t)} \left[\int_0^t f(u) f(t-u)\, du \right] dt = 0.$$

The repeated integral on the left may be rewritten as a double integral extended over the triangle $0 \le u \le t \le 2T$ in the u, t plane. We introduce new variables of integration, v, w, by the substitution $u = T - v$, $t = 2T - v - w$ and obtain

$$\iint_\triangle e^{n(v+w)} f(T-v) f(T-w)\, dv\, dw = 0, \tag{2}$$

where $\triangle$ is the triangle $v + w \ge 0$, $v \le T$, $w \le T$ in the v, w plane. Let $\triangle'$ be the triangle $v + w \le 0$, $v \ge -T$, $w \ge -T$. Then $\triangle + \triangle'$ is the square $-T \le v$, $w \le T$. (2) shows that the integral over $\triangle + \triangle'$ is equal to the integral over $\triangle'$; the integral over $\triangle + \triangle'$ is the product of two single integrals; and in the integral over $\triangle'$ we have $e^{n(v+w)} \le 1$. Thus we obtain

$$\left| \left[\int_{-T}^T e^{nu} f(T-u)\, du \right]^2 \right| = \left| \iint_{\triangle+\triangle'} e^{n(v+w)} f(T-v) f(T-w)\, dv\, dw \right|$$

$$= \left| \iint_{\triangle'} \right| \le \iint_{\triangle'} |f(T-v) f(T-w)|\, dv\, dw \le 2T^2 A^2$$

where A is an upper bound for $|f(t)|$ in $0 \le t \le 2T$, and $2T^2$ is the area of $\triangle'$. We then have

$$\left| \int_{-T}^T e^{nu} f(T-u)\, du \right| \le \sqrt{2}\, TA$$

and furthermore

$$\left| \int_{-T}^0 e^{nu} f(T-u)\, du \right| \le TA.$$

Consequently,

$$\left| \int_0^T e^{nu} f(T-u)\, du \right| = \left| \int_{-T}^T - \int_{-T}^0 \right| \le (1 + \sqrt{2})\, TA$$

for $n = 1, 2, \cdots$, and $f(t) = 0$ for $0 \le t \le T$ by lemma 2. This proves lemma 4, and the corollary follows since in this case both the assumptions and conclusion of lemma 4 hold for each $T > 0$.

We are now ready to prove theorem 2. Let $a, b \in \mathfrak{C}$ and

$$ab(t) = \int_0^t a(t-u)\, b(u)\, du = 0 \qquad \text{for} \qquad t \geq 0;$$

and set

$$a_n(t) = t^n\, a(t), \qquad b_n(t) = t^n\, b(t) \qquad\qquad n = 1, 2, \cdots.$$

Now,

$$\int_0^t (t-u)\, a(t-u)\, b(u)\, du + \int_0^t a(t-u)\, ub(u)\, du = \int_0^t t\, a(t-u)\, b(u)\, du = 0$$

for all $t \geq 0$, that is, $a_1 b + ab_1 = \{0\}$. Then also $ab_1\,(a_1 b + ab_1) = \{0\}$ and by theorem 1 this may be written as $(ab)\,(a_1 b_1) + (ab_1)^2 = \{0\}$. Furthermore, $ab = \{0\}$ so that we have $(ab_1)^2 = \{0\}$. Since $ab_1 \in \mathfrak{C}$, it follows from the corollary to lemma 4 that $ab_1 = \{0\}$. Repeating this argument we find that $ab_n = \{0\}$ for $n = 1, 2, \cdots$, or

$$\int_0^t u^n\, a(t-u)\, b(u)\, du = 0 \qquad\qquad n = 1, 2, \cdots.$$

Applying lemma 3, we find that $a(t-u)\, b(u) = 0$ for $0 \leq u \leq t$ and all $t \geq 0$. If there is a u_0 for which $b(u_0) \neq 0$, then $a(t-u_0) = 0$ for all $t \geq u_0$, or $a(v) = 0$ for all $v \geq 0$. Hence either $a(v) = 0$ for all $v \geq 0$ or $b(u) = 0$ for all $u \geq 0$. This completes the proof of theorem 2.

2.3 The Field of Convolution Quotients

The absence of divisors of zero in the convolution ring makes it possible to extend this ring to a field that will be denoted by $\mathfrak{F}$ and will be called the *field of convolution quotients*.

In this section $a, b, \cdots$ stand for continuous functions (elements of $\mathfrak{C}$) and $\alpha, \beta, \cdots$, for numbers (elements of $\mathfrak{N}$). Given a and b, $b \neq \{0\}$, the convolution equation $bz = a$ has at most one solution in $\mathfrak{C}$; if z_1 and z_2 are both solutions, then $b(z_1 - z_2) = bz_1 - bz_2 = a - a = \{0\}$ by theorem 1, and since $b \neq \{0\}$ it follows from theorem 2 that $z_1 - z_2 = \{0\}$ or $z_1(t) = z_2(t)$ for all $t \geq 0$. But, of course, the equation $bz = a$ may have no solution in $\mathfrak{C}$. For instance, if $a(0) \neq 0$ then there can be no solution, for bz, being a convolution of the form 2.1(1), certainly vanishes at $t = 0$.

An extended algebraic system, a *quotient field*, can now be constructed in which the equation $bx = a$, $b \neq \{0\}$, always has a solution. The construction follows closely the construction of rational numbers in terms of ordered pairs of integers, and readers familiar with that construction will find it unnecessary to follow in detail the verifications carried out in this construction.

The construction is carried out in terms of *ordered pairs*, (a, b), of continuous functions in which it is always assumed that $b \neq \{0\}$; this ordered pair will correspond to the solution of $bz = a$.

DEFINITION 3. (i) (a, b) and (c, d) are equivalent if $ad = bc$, (ii) $\frac{a}{b}$ or a/b is the class of all ordered pairs equivalent to (a, b). Each such class is called an *equivalence class* or a *convolution quotient*; and each ordered pair belonging to a/b is called a *representative* of a/b or is said to represent a/b.

The relation established by definition 3 (i) is a true *equivalence relation*: it is *reflexive*—that is, (a, b) is equivalent to (a, b); *symmetric*, if (a, b) is equivalent to (c, d) then also (c, d) will be equivalent to (a, b); and *transitive*, if (a, b) is equivalent to (c, d) and (c, d) is equivalent to (e, f), then (a, b) will be equivalent to (e, f). The first two of these properties follow easily from the properties of convolution given in theorem 1. To prove transitivity, we remark that $d \neq \{0\}$, and by theorem 2, $af - be = 0$ if and only if $d(af - be) = 0$. Now, $ad = bc$, $cf = de$, and using the commutativity and associativity of convolution, $daf = (ad)f = (bc)f = b(cf) = b(de) = dbe$. It follows that the set of all ordered pairs is broken up into equivalence classes. Each ordered pair belongs to precisely one equivalence class and may be regarded as a *representative* of that equivalence class.

DEFINITION 4. (i) The set of all equivalence classes is called the *field of convolution quotients*, and will be denoted by $\mathfrak{F}$. (ii) The operations of addition, multiplication by a scalar, and convolution in $\mathfrak{F}$ are defined by the equations

$$\frac{a}{b} + \frac{c}{d} = \frac{ad + bc}{bd}, \qquad \alpha \frac{a}{b} = \frac{\alpha a}{b}, \qquad \frac{a}{b}\frac{c}{d} = \frac{ac}{bd}.$$

In order to make the second part of this definition meaningful, we have to show that the operations thus defined are truly operations on equivalence classes and are independent of the representatives chosen for each equivalence class. In the case of addition, for instance, we have to deduce from $a/b = a'/b'$ and $c/d = c'/d'$ that $(ad + bc)/(bd) = (a'd' + b'c')/(b'd')$. Now, if $ab' = a'b$ and $cd' = c'd$, then $(ad + bc)b'd' = ab'dd' + bb'cd' = a'bdd' + bb'c'd = (a'd' + b'c')bd$, and this proves the required property. The corresponding property of the other two operations can be proved similarly.

THEOREM 3.

(i) $\dfrac{a}{b} = \dfrac{c}{d}$ if and only if $ad = bc$;

(ii) $\dfrac{a}{b} + \dfrac{c}{d} = \dfrac{c}{d} + \dfrac{a}{b}$, $\dfrac{a}{b} + \left(\dfrac{c}{d} + \dfrac{e}{f}\right) = \left(\dfrac{a}{b} + \dfrac{c}{d}\right) + \dfrac{e}{f}$;

(iii) $\alpha\left(\dfrac{a}{b}+\dfrac{c}{d}\right)=\alpha\dfrac{a}{b}+\alpha\dfrac{c}{d}\,,\qquad (\alpha+\beta)\dfrac{a}{b}=\alpha\dfrac{a}{b}+\beta\dfrac{a}{b}\,;$

$\alpha\left(\dfrac{a}{b}\dfrac{c}{d}\right)=\left(\alpha\dfrac{a}{b}\right)\dfrac{c}{d}=\dfrac{a}{b}\left(\alpha\dfrac{c}{d}\right),\qquad (\alpha\beta)\dfrac{a}{b}=\alpha\left(\beta\dfrac{a}{b}\right);$

(iv) $\dfrac{a}{b}\dfrac{c}{d}=\dfrac{c}{d}\dfrac{a}{b}\,,\qquad \dfrac{a}{b}\left(\dfrac{c}{d}\dfrac{e}{f}\right)=\left(\dfrac{a}{b}\dfrac{c}{d}\right)\dfrac{e}{f}\,,$

$\left(\dfrac{a}{b}+\dfrac{c}{d}\right)\dfrac{e}{f}=\dfrac{a}{b}\dfrac{e}{f}+\dfrac{c}{d}\dfrac{e}{f}\,;$

(v)   if $e\neq\{0\}$ and $f\neq\{0\}$ then $\dfrac{a}{b}=\dfrac{c}{d}$ if and only if $\dfrac{a}{b}\dfrac{e}{f}=\dfrac{c}{d}\dfrac{e}{f}\,.$

Proof. (i) $a/b=c/d$ means that the equivalence classes determined by (a, b) and (c, d) are identical, and this is the case if and only if (a, b) and (c, d) are equivalent. The proofs of (ii) to (iv) follow easily from theorem 1. These statements express the commutative, associative, and distributive properties of the algebraic operations in $\mathfrak{F}$. (v) is the *cancellation law:* it holds in $\mathfrak{C}$ by theorem 2 and its validity in $\mathfrak{F}$ can be deduced from theorem 2.

THEOREM 4. $\mathfrak{F}$ is both a *vector space* (under addition and multiplication by scalars) and a *field* (under addition and convolution); thus, $\mathfrak{F}$ is an *algebra*. The *zero element* of $\mathfrak{F}$ is the convolution quotient $\{0\}/b$, $b\neq\{0\}$ and the *unit element*, b/b, $b\neq\{0\}$.

Proof. (i) $\{0\}/b=\{0\}/c$ so that $\{0\}/b$ defines a unique element of $\mathfrak{F}$, and

$$\dfrac{\{0\}}{b}+\dfrac{c}{d}=\dfrac{\{0\}\,d+bc}{bd}=\dfrac{bc}{bd}=\dfrac{c}{d}\,,\qquad \dfrac{\{0\}}{b}\dfrac{c}{d}=\dfrac{\{0\}\,c}{bd}=\dfrac{\{0\}}{bd}=\dfrac{\{0\}}{b}\,.$$

(ii) $b/b=c/c$ so that b/b defines a unique element of $\mathfrak{F}$ and

$$\dfrac{b}{b}\dfrac{c}{d}=\dfrac{bc}{bd}=\dfrac{c}{d}\,.$$

(iii) It is easy to verify from theorem 3 (ii), (iii) that $\mathfrak{F}$ endowed with the operations of addition and multiplication by scalars is a vector space over $\mathfrak{R}$ with $\{0\}/b$ as the zero vector. (iv) In order to prove that $\mathfrak{F}$ endowed with the operations of addition and convolution forms a field, we have to verify that division can be performed in $\mathfrak{F}$ with the sole exception of division by the zero element. If $a/b\,\epsilon\,\mathfrak{F}$, $c/d\,\epsilon\,\mathfrak{F}$ and $c\neq\{0\}$, then $(c/d)\,(x/y)=a/b$ has at least one solution, namely $x/y=(ad)/(bc)$. Suppose that x'/y' is also a solution. Then $(c/d)\,(x/y)=a/b=(c/d)\,(x'/y')$ and since $c\neq\{0\}$, we have $x/y=x'/y'$ by the cancellation law. Thus division by a nonzero element of $\mathfrak{F}$ is always possible and leads to a unique result. It is now easy to verify that $\mathfrak{F}$ is a field and b/b, the unit element of the field.

From now on we shall frequently denote an element of $\mathfrak{F}$ by a single letter.

In case of doubt we shall indicate whether a symbol like a stands for a continuous function ($a \in \mathfrak{C}$) or a convolution quotient ($a \in \mathfrak{F}$).

PROBLEMS

1. Verify that

$$\frac{\{e^t - \sin t - \cos t\}}{\{\sin t\}} = \{2e^t\}.$$

2. Verify that multiplication by a scalar and convolution in $\mathfrak{F}$ as defined in definition 4 are operations on equivalence classes.

3. Prove theorem 3 (iii).

4. Carry out in detail step (iii) in the proof of theorem 4. (You may use theorem 3 in the proof.)

2.4 Properties of $\mathfrak{F}$

The elements of $\mathfrak{F}$ are abstract entities and in general it does not seem possible to give a pictorial description of them. Nevertheless, it will turn out that some elements of $\mathfrak{F}$ correspond to numbers, others to (continuous or discontinuous) functions, while yet others correspond to operators of differentiation or integration. We may thus regard convolution quotients either as *generalized functions* or else as *operators*. This dual nature of convolution quotients sounds at first confusing and artificial, but in the long run it simplifies matters in that everything involved in operational calculus belongs to one algebraic system (instead of having functions, impulse functions, and operators as separate entities).

Given two sets, A and B, endowed with certain algebraic operations, we say that A can be *embedded* in B if (i) every algebraic operation in A has its counterpart in B, and (ii) there exists a one-to-one correspondence between the elements of A and some elements of B which preserves the algebraic operations; and we shall indicate by $a \Leftrightarrow b$, $a \in A$, $b \in B$, such a correspondence. For instance, the ring of integers can be embedded in this sense in the field of rational numbers.

We shall show that $\mathfrak{N}$ and $\mathfrak{C}$ can be embedded in $\mathfrak{F}$, that is, that real or complex numbers and continuous functions can be identified with certain convolution quotients, and we shall also show that such an identification can be established for certain discontinuous functions.

DEFINITION 5. (i) A function of the nonnegative real variable t which is absolutely integrable over $0 \le t \le t_0$ for each $t_0 > 0$ is called a *locally integrable* function. (ii) Two locally integrable functions are said to be *equivalent* if their indefinite integrals differ by a constant. (iii) The collection of all equivalence classes of locally integrable functions will be denoted by $\mathfrak{R}$.

The notion of local integrability clearly depends on the integration theory one uses. Adopting the integration theory outlined in section 1.5, local integrability in the sense of definition 5(i) coincides with local integrability on the semi-infinite interval $t \geq 0$ in the sense of section 1.5. It follows from theorem A of that section that two locally integrable functions are equivalent if and only if they are equal at their points of continuity, that is to say, equal except at a set of isolated points. (If Lebesgue's theory of integration is used, equivalence of two locally integrable functions is tantamount to equality almost everywhere.) The property defined in (ii) is a true equivalence relation: it is easily seen to be reflexive, symmetric, and transitive, and hence to divide the set of all locally integrable functions into equivalence classes. We shall regard equivalent locally integrable functions as being identical from our point of view and accordingly will make no sharp distinction between a locally integrable function f and the equivalence class of which f is a representative. In this sense we shall write, somewhat inexactly, $f \epsilon \Re$ although the equivalence class containing f rather than f itself is an element of $\Re$.

Every continuous function is locally integrable and thus there exists a *natural embedding* of $\mathfrak{C}$ in $\Re$.

Definition 2 of addition and multiplication by a scalar can be extended to locally integrable functions, and $\Re$ equipped with these operations is clearly a vector space. According to section 1.5, theorem B, convolution can also be defined for locally integrable functions and is clearly an operation on equivalence classes of locally integrable functions so that $\Re$ is also a commutative ring. Thus, $\Re$ is an algebra. Moreover, it is easy to show that for c in $\mathfrak{C}$ and f in $\Re$, the convolution $cf(t)$ exists for every $t \geq 0$ and defines a continuous function (see problem 6). (In algebraical language, $\mathfrak{C}$ is an *ideal* in $\Re$.)

In particular, $hf = \{\int_0^t f(u)\, du\}$ is in $\mathfrak{C}$ for f in $\Re$ and clearly remains unchanged if f is replaced by an equivalent function.

THEOREM 5. (i) $\alpha \Leftrightarrow \alpha h/h$ defines an embedding of $\mathfrak{N}$ in $\mathfrak{F}$. (ii) $c \Leftrightarrow hc/h$ defines an embedding of $\mathfrak{C}$ in $\mathfrak{F}$. (iii) $f \Leftrightarrow hf/h$ defines an embedding of $\Re$ in $\mathfrak{F}$.

Proof. (i) By straightforward computation,

$$\frac{\alpha h}{h} + \frac{\beta h}{h} = \frac{(\alpha + \beta)h}{h}, \qquad \frac{\alpha h}{h}\frac{\beta h}{h} = \frac{\alpha\beta h^2}{h^2} = \frac{(\alpha\beta)h}{h}, \qquad \frac{\dfrac{\alpha h}{h}}{\dfrac{\beta h}{h}} = \frac{\left(\dfrac{\alpha}{\beta}\right)h}{h}$$

so that the one-to-one mapping $\alpha \Leftrightarrow \alpha h/h$ of $\mathfrak{N}$ into $\mathfrak{F}$ preserves the algebraic operations on complex numbers and defines an embedding. If $b \epsilon \mathfrak{C}$ and $b \neq \{0\}$ then clearly $(\alpha h)/h = (\alpha b)/b$, so that the same embedding may be defined also by $\alpha \Leftrightarrow (\alpha b)/b$ with an arbitrary b. (ii) Virtually the same computation shows that the mapping $c \Leftrightarrow (ch)/h$ preserves the algebraic operations in $\mathfrak{C}$ and can also be represented by $c \Leftrightarrow (cb)/b$ where $b \epsilon \mathfrak{C}$ and $b \neq \{0\}$. (iii) Again the same computation can be used to show that the mapping $f \Leftrightarrow (hf)/h$ preserves the algebraic operations in $\mathfrak{R}$. If the result of problem 6 is known, the same embedding can also be described by $f \Leftrightarrow (bf)/b$ with $b \epsilon \mathfrak{C}$, $b \neq \{0\}$.

The number 0, the continuous function $\{0\}$, and the convolution quotient $\{0\}/b$ are conceptually different but they behave in the same manner under algebraic operations, and are identified under our embeddings: from now on they will be denoted by the same symbol 0. Similarly, any number α and the corresponding convolution quotient $(\alpha h)/h$, although conceptually different, are operationally equivalent and will be denoted by the same symbol α: Mikusiński calls these convolution quotients *numerical operators*. In particular, 1 stands either for the number "one" or for the unit element of $\mathfrak{F}$. The relation $1 \cdot f = f$, with 1 interpreted as the unit element of $\mathfrak{F}$, expresses the sifting property of the delta function, thus showing that 1, regarded as a generalized function, is our substitute for the delta function. It may be mentioned here that a nonzero number α and the continuous function $\{\alpha\} = \alpha h$ are essentially different, they behave differently under convolution, and must not be confused. For instance, 1 is the delta function, while $\{1\} = h$ is the restriction of Heaviside's unit function to $t \geq 0$.

Similarly, the (continuous or locally integrable) function f and convolution quotient $(hf)/h$ will be identified and denoted by the same letter.

The embedding of continuous and locally integrable functions, and of the delta function, in $\mathfrak{F}$ suggests that convolution quotients be regarded as *generalized functions*. It is natural to ask whether such a generalized function can, under certain circumstances, have a definite *value* at a specified point t_0. The answer is in the negative, for two locally integrable functions which differ only at t_0 correspond to the same convolution quotient. In this respect the continuous function $\{1\}$ and the corresponding convolution quotient h are different. h represents not only the continuous function $\{1\}$ but also every locally integrable function which is equal to 1 almost everywhere. Nevertheless, under certain circumstances, it is possible to associate with a generalized function values on an *interval*. In this sense we shall write $f(t)$ for $t \epsilon I$ even if f is not a function.

DEFINITION 6. For an open interval I: $t_1 < t < t_2$ with $0 \leq t_1 < t_2 \leq \infty$, $f \epsilon \mathfrak{F}$, and ϕ a (numerical-valued) function on I, we say that $f(t) = \phi(t)$ on I or for $t \epsilon I$ if for some nonnegative integer n, $h^n f \epsilon \mathfrak{C}$, $h^n f(t)$ is n times differentiable on I, and

$$\frac{d^n}{dt^n} h^n f(t) = \phi(t) \qquad\qquad t \epsilon I. \qquad (1)$$

If $f \epsilon \mathfrak{C}$, definition 6 can be applied with $n = 0$ and $\phi(t) = f(t)$, thus showing that in this case the value of the generalized function f coincides with the value in the usual sense. If $f \epsilon \mathfrak{R}$, we may apply definition 6 with $n = 1$. In this case $d[h f(t)]/dt = f(t)$ on every interval on which f is continuous so that here too we find agreement between the value of f in the usual sense and the value according to definition 6.

THEOREM 6. $\phi(t)$, if it exists, is unique.

Proof. Suppose that

$$\frac{d^m}{dt^m} h^m f(t) = \phi_1(t), \qquad \frac{d^n}{dt^n} h^n f(t) = \phi_2(t) \qquad\qquad t \in I$$

and $n > m$. Since $h^n f = h^{n-m}(h^m f)$ is the $n-m$ times repeated integral of the continuous function $h^m f$, $h^n f$ is $n-m$ times continuously differentiable, and

$$\frac{d^{n-m}}{dt^{n-m}} h^n f(t) = h^m f(t)$$

Thus,

$$\phi_2(t) = \frac{d^m}{dt^m} \left(\frac{d^{n-m}}{dt^{n-m}} h^n f(t) \right) = \frac{d^m}{dt^m} h^m f(t) = \phi_1(t). \qquad\qquad t \in I.$$

Definition 6 is restricted to those convolution quotients of the form c/h^n, $c \in \mathfrak{C}$. These are, apart from the absence of a growth restriction on c, the *perfect operators* introduced by Weston (1957, 1959), and they include most of the familiar impulse functions. It should be stressed, though, that not all such generalized functions possess values on some interval. For instance, if c is a nondifferentiable continuous function, and $f = c/h$, then it is easy to see $h^n f$, while continuous for each $n \geq 1$, is not n times differentiable for any n or on any interval, so that f does not possess values, according to definition 6, on any interval.

To show that generalized functions may possess values according to definition 6 even if they are not functions, let us denote for the moment the unit element of $\mathfrak{F}$ by δ. Then $h\delta = h \in \mathfrak{C}$ and is differentiable for $t > 0$, moreover, $d[h\delta(t)]/dt = 0$ for $t > 0$, so that $\delta(t) = 0$ for $t > 0$.

So far we have thought of convolution quotients as generalized functions. Alternatively, we can think of them as operators. It has been pointed out in section 2.1 that h may be regarded as the operator of integration when applied to a continuous function. It is natural to regard h as the operator of integration for generalized functions too so that for any $f \in \mathfrak{F}$, hf is the integral "from 0 to t" of f, this integral itself being, in general, a generalized function. Moreover, h possesses a reciprocal in $\mathfrak{F}$, and we shall expect that $h^{-1} = b/(bh)$, $b \in \mathfrak{C}$, $b \neq 0$, is in some sense the operator of differentiation. This aspect of convolution quotients as operators of differentiation and integration will be explored in greater detail in the next chapter.

PROBLEMS

1. Carry out in detail the proof of theorem 5 (ii).

2. Which of the functions listed in section 2.1, problem 1, belong to $\mathfrak{R}$?

3. Re $\alpha \geq 1$, Re $\beta \geq 1$, and $f = h^\alpha/h^\beta$. Show that $f \in \mathfrak{C}$ if $\alpha = \beta + 1$ or Re $\alpha >$ Re $\beta + 1$; and that $f \in \mathfrak{R}$ if Re $\alpha >$ Re β. Evaluate f in the latter case.

4. Discuss f of problem 3 when $\alpha = \beta$ or $\alpha = \beta - 1$.

5. f being defined as in the two preceding problems, show that

$$f(t) = \frac{t^{\alpha-\beta-1}}{\Gamma(\alpha - \beta)} \quad \text{for} \quad t > 0$$

and in particular, that $f(t) = 0$ for $t > 0$ if $a - \beta - 1$ is a negative integer.

6. If $c \; \epsilon \; \mathfrak{C}$ and $f \; \epsilon \; \mathfrak{R}$, show that

$$\int_0^t c(t - u) f(u) \, du$$

exists for every $t \geq 0$ and defines a continuous function of t.

7. Show that the mapping defined by assigning to each locally integrable function f the continuous function hf is a one-to-one mapping of $\mathfrak{R}$ onto a proper subset of $\mathfrak{C}$. Can you identify this subset?

8. Show that the mapping defined in the preceding problem preserves the vector space operations but fails to preserve convolution.

[3]

Applications to Differential and Integral Equations

3.1 The Operator *s*

We have seen in section 2.1 that h is the operator of integration and h^n that of n times repeated integration. We have also defined h^α for Re $\alpha > 0$. We now extend the definition of h^α to all $\alpha \in \Re$ by setting $h^\alpha = h^{\alpha+n}/h^n$, where n is the least positive integer for which Re $\alpha + n > 1$. 2.1(4) proves that this definition is consistent with 2.1(3) when Re $\alpha > 0$, that $h^0 = 1$, and that equation 2.1(4) holds for the so extended h^α for all values of α and β.

In particular, we shall study

$$s = h^{-1} = \frac{h}{h^2}. \tag{1}$$

For this operator we have

$$s^0 = 1, \qquad s^\alpha = h^{-\alpha}, \qquad s^\alpha s^\beta = s^{\alpha+\beta}. \tag{2}$$

s is the operator of differentiation as will be seen from theorem 7.

For a differentiable function $a = \{a(t)\}$ we set $a^{(k)} = \{d^k a(t)/dt^k\}, k = 0, 1, 2, \cdots$, and we shall say that such a function possesses a locally integrable nth derivative if a is $n - 1$ times continuously differentiable, $a^{(n-1)}$ is differentiable except on a set of isolated points, and $a^{(n)}$ is locally integrable. According to theorem A of section 1.5,

$$\int_\alpha^\beta a^{(k)}(u)\, du = a^{(k-1)}(\beta) - a^{(k-1)}(\alpha)$$

holds for such a function for $k = 1, 2, \cdots, n$ and all nonnegative α and β.

THEOREM 7. If $a = \{a(t)\}$ possesses a locally integrable derivative of order n then

$$s^n a = a^{(n)} + a^{(n-1)}(0) + a^{(n-2)}(0)\, s + \cdots + a(0)\, s^{n-1}. \tag{3}$$

Proof. First assume $n = 1$. Since $a(t)$ possesses a locally integrable derivative, we have

$$a(t) = a(0) + \int_0^t a'(u)\, du$$

28

or

$$a = a(0)\, h + a'h,$$

and upon multiplication by s,

$$sa = a' + a(0), \tag{4}$$

thus proving (3) for $n = 1$. We now complete the proof of the theorem by induction. Suppose (3) holds for $n - 1$ so that

$$s^{n-1}\, b = b^{(n-1)} + b^{(n-2)}(0) + b^{(n-3)}(0)\, s + \cdots + b(0)\, s^{n-2}$$

provided that $b(t)$ possesses a locally integrable derivative of order $n - 1$; and apply this relation to $b = a' = sa - a(0)$ (which has, by assumption, a locally integrable derivative of order $n - 1$). Clearly, $b^{(k)} = a^{(k+1)}$ and hence

$$s^{n-1}\, b = s^n\, a - a(0)\, s^{n-1} = a^{(n)} + a^{(n-1)}(0) + \cdots + a'(0)\, s^{n-2},$$

thus completing the proof of the theorem.

For a function satisfying the conditions of theorem 7 we have $s^n a = a^{(n)}$ provided that $a(0) = a'(0) = \cdots = a^{(n-1)}(0) = 0$. If either the differentiability condition or the "initial conditions" fail, $s^n f$ will not be a function but it will always exist as a generalized function whenever a itself is a generalized function. We shall regard $s^n a$ as the *extended* derivative of order n of a. [The adjective "extended" refers to the circumstance that in the case of a differentiable function a, $s^n a$ incorporates the values of a, a', $\cdots$, $a^{(n-1)}$ at the origin with the function $a^{(n)}$.] For a function satisfying the conditions of theorem 7, $s^n a$ and $a^{(n)}$ differ at most by a polynomial of degree $n - 1$ in s; for other differentiable functions the relation between $s^n a$ and $a^{(n)}$ may be more complicated.

We shall conclude this section with several examples illustrating the relation between a and $s^\alpha a$ in cases where theorem 7 does not apply directly. In two of these examples we shall make use of the notations

$$\operatorname{sgn} x = \begin{cases} 1 & \text{if} & x > 0 \\ 0 & \text{if} & x = 0 \\ -1 & \text{if} & x < 0 \end{cases} \tag{5}$$

and $h_\alpha(x) = h^{\alpha-1}\, \{H(t - x)\}$. In the latter, $x > 0$, H is Heaviside's unit function defined in 1.3(3), and α is any complex number. [$h_\alpha(x)$ will be discussed in greater detail in chapter 4.]

EXAMPLE 1. To find sf and $s^2 f$ when $f = \{t^2|t - 1|\}$.

$$f(t) = t^2|t - 1| = \begin{cases} t^2 - t^3 & \text{if} & 0 \leq t \leq 1 \\ t^3 - t^2 & \text{if} & 1 \leq t \end{cases}$$

is clearly continuous for $t \geq 0$ and is continuously differentiable except at $t = 1$. By theorem 7

$$sf = \{f'(t)\} = \begin{cases} 2t - 3t^2 & 0 \leq t < 1 \\ 3t^2 - 2t & 1 < t \end{cases} = \{(3t^2 - 2t) \operatorname{sgn} (t - 1)\}.$$

Theorem 7 cannot be applied directly to the evaluation of s^2f since $f' = sf$ is discontinuous. Noting that the only discontinuity of f' is a jump at $t = 1$, we consider $\{f'(t) - 2H(t - 1)\}$ which is a continuous function for $t \geq 0$ and is continuously differentiable except at $t = 1$. By theorem 7

$$s\{f'(t) - 2H(t - 1)\} = s \begin{cases} 2t - 3t^2 & 0 \leq t \leq 1 \\ 3t^2 - 2t - 2 & 1 \leq t \end{cases}$$

$$= \begin{cases} 2 - 6t & 0 \leq t < 1 \\ 6t - 2 & 1 < t \end{cases}$$

so that

$$s^2f = sf' = s\{f'(t) - 2H(t - 1)\} + 2h_0(1) = 2\{(3t - 1) \operatorname{sgn} (t - 1)\} + 2h_0(1).$$

EXAMPLE 2. To find s^2f when $f(t) = \phi(t + x) + \phi(|t - x|)$, $x > 0$, and ϕ is twice continuously differentiable.

As in example 1, we have by theorem 7

$sf = \{\phi'(t + x) + \phi'(|t - x|) \operatorname{sgn} (t - x)\} + 2\phi(x) = g + 2\phi(x)$, say. If $\phi'(0) \neq 0$, g has a jump discontinuity at $t = x$, but $\{g(t) - 2\phi'(0) H(t - x)\}$ is continuous, $g(0) - 2\phi'(0) H(- x) = 0$, and

$$s[g - 2\phi'(0) h_1(x)] = s\{\phi'(t + x) + \phi'(|t - x|) \operatorname{sgn} (t - x) - 2\phi'(0) H(t - x)\}$$
$$= \{\phi''(t + x) + \phi''(|t - x|)\}$$

by theorem 7. Thus,

$$s^2f = s[g + 2\phi(x)] = s[g - 2\phi'(0) h_1(x)] + 2\phi'(0) h_0(x) + 2\phi(x) s$$
$$= \{\phi''(t + x) + \phi''(|t - x|)\} + 2\phi'(0) h_0(x) + 2\phi(x) s.$$

EXAMPLE 3. For Re $\alpha < 0$, $s^\alpha = \{t^{-\alpha-1}/\Gamma(- \alpha)\}$, and

$$\Gamma(- \alpha) s^\alpha f(t) = \int_0^t (t - u)^{-\alpha-1} f(u) \, du \qquad \text{Re } \alpha < 0 \tag{6}$$

for $f \epsilon \Re$. This relation does not hold, and in fact the integral is in general divergent, if Re $\alpha \geq 0$. Nevertheless, in certain cases (6) is not completely meaningless. Suppose that n is a positive integer, $n - 1 < \text{Re } \alpha < n$, f is n times continuously differentiable, and $f(0) = f'(0) = \cdots = f^{(n-1)}(0) = 0$ so that $s^n f = f^{(n)}$ by theorem 7.

Then

$$\Gamma(-\alpha)\, s^{\alpha} = \Gamma(-\alpha)\, h^{n-\alpha}\, s^{n} = \frac{\Gamma(-\alpha)}{\Gamma(n-\alpha)} \{t^{n-\alpha-1}\}\, s^{n}$$

and

$$\Gamma(-\alpha)\, s^{\alpha} f = \frac{\Gamma(-\alpha)}{\Gamma(n-\alpha)} \{t^{n-\alpha-1}\}\, f^{(n)}$$

is a continuous function whose value at t,

$$\frac{\Gamma(-\alpha)}{\Gamma(n-\alpha)} \int_{0}^{t} (t-u)^{n-\alpha-1} f^{(n)}(u)\, du$$

is the *finite part* of the divergent integral on the right of (5). [See Butzer (1959) for the application of operational calculus to the finite parts of divergent integrals.]

PROBLEMS

1. Show that for all $\alpha \in \mathfrak{N}$

$$h^{\alpha}(t) - \frac{t^{\alpha-1}}{\Gamma(\alpha)} \qquad\qquad t > 0$$

in the sense of definition 6.

2. If $f \in \mathfrak{C}$ and either $\alpha = n$ or $\operatorname{Re}\alpha > n$, $n = 1, 2, \cdots$, prove that $g = h^{\alpha} f$ is an n times continuously differentiable function for which $g(0) = g'(0) = \cdots = g^{(n-1)}(0) = 0$. Evaluate $g^{(n)}$ in terms of f.
Obtain corresponding results for $h^{\alpha} f$ when $f \in \mathfrak{R}$.

3. If f is n times continuously differentiable, $f(0) = f'(0) = \cdots = f^{(n-1)}(0) = 0$, and $\operatorname{Re}\alpha < n$, show that $s^{\alpha} f \in \mathfrak{C}$, and evaluate this function.

4. Evaluate

(i) $(\alpha s^{2} + \beta)\{\cos \omega t\}$,   (ii) $s^{2}\{at + \beta\}$

where α, β, and ω are numbers.

5. For an n times continuously differentiable function f, and $n - 1 < \operatorname{Re}\alpha < n$, the finite part of the divergent integral

$$\int_{0}^{t} (t-u)^{-\alpha-1} f(u)\, du$$

is defined as

$$FP \int_{0}^{t} (t-u)^{-\alpha-1} f(u)\, du$$

$$= \sum_{k=1}^{n} \frac{\Gamma(-\alpha)}{\Gamma(k-\alpha)}\, t^{k-\alpha-1} f^{(k-1)}(0) + \frac{\Gamma(-\alpha)}{\Gamma(n-\alpha)} \int_{0}^{t} (t-u)^{n-\alpha-1} f^{(n)}(u)\, du.$$

Establish a connection between this finite part and the convolution quotient $\Gamma(-\alpha) s^\alpha f$, and show in particular that

$$\Gamma(-\alpha) s^\alpha f(t) = FP \int_0^t (t-u)^{-\alpha-1} f(u)\, du \qquad\qquad t > 0$$

in the sense of definition 6.

6. For a continuously differentiable function f, the finite part of the divergent integral

$$\int_0^t f(u)\, \frac{du}{t-u}$$

is defined as

$$f(0) \log t + \int_0^t f'(u) \log (t-u)\, du.$$

Establish a connection between this finite part and the convolution quotient $s\{\log t\}f$.

7. Suppose that $f(t) = \phi(t)$ on I in the sense of definition 6, and $\phi(t)$ is k times continuously differentiable on I. Prove that $s^k f(t) = \phi^{(k)}(t)$ on I. Deduce that for a locally integrable function f that is n times continuously differentiable for $t > 0$ we have $s^n f(t) = f^{(n)}(t)$ for $t > 0$.

8. Evaluate $s^2 f$ when (i) $f(t) = \phi(x+t) + \phi(|x-t|)\,\mathrm{sgn}\,(x-t)$, $x > 0$, and ϕ is twice continuously differentiable; (ii)

$$f(t) = \int_{|x-t|}^{x+t} \phi(y)\, dy,$$

$x > 0$, and ϕ is continuously differentiable.

9. The function f is continuous except at $t = x > 0$ where it has a jump discontinuity, and f possesses a locally integrable derivative. Show that

$$sf = f' + f(0) + [f(x+) - f(x-)]\, h_0(x),$$

where

$$f(x+) = \lim f(x + \epsilon), \qquad f(x-) = \lim f(x - \epsilon) \tag{7}$$

as $\epsilon \to 0$ through positive values.

Formulate and prove a similar result for $s^2 f$ under appropriate assumptions on f. Deduce the answers to examples 1 and 2 and to problem 8 from your result.

3.2 Rational Functions of s

$1 = sh = s\{1\}$ so that the delta function is the extended derivative of Heaviside's unit function. $s = s \cdot 1$, $s^2 = s^2 \cdot 1$, $\cdots$, are the extended derivatives of the delta function. Any *polynomial* in s, such as

$$p = \alpha_0 + \alpha_1 s + \cdots + \alpha_m s^m \qquad\qquad \alpha_0, \cdots, \alpha_m \in \mathfrak{R}$$

is an *impulse function*. We shall show that $p(t) = 0$ for $t > 0$ for such a function. Indeed, let n be a positive integer and $n > m$. Then

$$q = h^n p = \sum_{k=0}^{m} \alpha_k h^{n-k} = \left\{ \sum_{k=0}^{m} \frac{\alpha_k}{(n-k-1)!} \, t^{n-k-1} \right\} \in \mathfrak{C}$$

and is in fact a polynomial of degree $n - 1$. Thus, q is n times differentiable, and $q^{(n)}(t) = 0$, for $t > 0$.

We now turn to certain *fractions* involving s. From 3.1(4),

$$s\{e^{\alpha t}\} = \{\alpha e^{\alpha t}\} + 1$$

or

$$(s - \alpha) \, \{e^{\alpha t}\} = 1,$$

so that

$$(s - \alpha)^{-1} = \{e^{\alpha t}\}. \qquad\qquad (1)$$

We can now prove by induction that

$$(s - \alpha)^{-n} = \left\{ \frac{t^{n-1} e^{\alpha t}}{(n-1)!} \right\} \qquad\qquad n = 1, 2, \cdots \qquad (2)$$

If (2) holds for $n - 1$, then

$$(s - \alpha)^{-n} = (s - \alpha)^{-1} (s - \alpha)^{-(n-1)} = \{e^{\alpha t}\} \left\{ \frac{t^{n-2} e^{\alpha t}}{(n-2)!} \right\}$$

$$= \left\{ \int_0^t e^{\alpha(t-u)} \frac{u^{n-2} e^{\alpha u}}{(n-2)!} \, du \right\} = \left\{ \frac{t^{n-1} e^{\alpha t}}{(n-1)!} \right\}$$

thus establishing (2).

We are now ready to interpret any *rational function* of s, such as

$$p = \frac{\alpha_0 + \alpha_1 s + \cdots + \alpha_m s^m}{\beta_0 + \beta_1 s + \cdots + \beta_n s^n}$$

where $\alpha_0, \cdots, \alpha_m, \beta_0, \cdots, \beta_n \in \mathfrak{R}$. Since the algebraic operations in $\mathfrak{F}$ obey the commutative, associative, and distributive laws, we may manipulate rational functions as in ordinary algebra. First we use long division to decompose p in a polynomial and a fraction whose denominator is of higher degree than the numerator. The polynomial is an impulse function. In the fraction, we factorize the denominator, decompose the fraction in partial fractions, and interpret each term according to (2). Clearly, p is a continuous function of t, indeed a combination of polynomials multiplied by exponential functions, if $n > m$.

EXAMPLE

$$\frac{s^4}{s^3 - 1} = s + \frac{s}{s^3 - 1} = s + \frac{s}{(s - 1)(s - \omega)(s - \omega^2)},$$

where

$$\omega = \frac{-1 + i\sqrt{3}}{2}, \qquad \omega^2 = \frac{-1 - i\sqrt{3}}{2}$$

are the complex cube roots of unity. Decomposition in partial fractions yields

$$\frac{s^4}{s^3 - 1} = s + \frac{1}{3}\left(\frac{1}{s - 1} + \frac{\omega^2}{s - \omega} + \frac{\omega}{s - \omega^2}\right)$$

or

$$\frac{s^4}{s^3 - 1} = s + \frac{1}{3}\left\{e^t + \omega^2 e^{\omega t} + \omega e^{\omega^2 t}\right\}$$

$$= s + \frac{1}{3}\left\{e^t - e^{-t/2}\cos\frac{\sqrt{3}}{2}t + \sqrt{3}\,e^{-t/2}\sin\frac{\sqrt{3}}{2}t\right\},$$

and finally

$$\frac{s^4}{s^3 - 1} = s + \left\{\frac{1}{3}e^t + \frac{2}{3}e^{-t/2}\cos\left(\frac{\sqrt{3}}{2}t - \frac{2\pi}{3}\right)\right\}.$$

It may be noted that for a complex parameter s, Euler's integral of the second kind gives

$$\int_0^\infty \frac{t^{n-1}}{(n-1)!}e^{\alpha t}e^{-st}\,dt = (s - \alpha)^{-n}$$

so that formally, (2) is in accordance with the Laplace transform interpretation of $(s - \alpha)^{-n}$. The reason for this coincidence will appear later: meanwhile this coincidence may be utilized by using available tables of inverse Laplace transforms [Gardner and Barnes (1942), Doetsch *et al.* (1947), Erdélyi *et al.* (1954)] as labor-saving devices.

PROBLEMS

1. Verify the following formulas:—

(i) $\dfrac{\lambda s + \mu}{(s + \alpha)^2 + \beta^2} = \left\{ \lambda e^{-\alpha t} \cos \beta t + \dfrac{\mu - \alpha\lambda}{\beta} e^{-\alpha t} \sin \beta t \right\}$

(ii) $\dfrac{\lambda s + \mu}{(s + \alpha)(s + \beta)} = \left\{ \dfrac{\alpha\lambda - \mu}{\alpha - \beta} e^{-\alpha t} + \dfrac{\beta\lambda - \mu}{\beta - \alpha} e^{-\beta t} \right\}$

(iii) $\dfrac{Q(s)}{P(s)} = \left\{ \displaystyle\sum_{m=1}^{n} \dfrac{Q(\alpha_m)}{P_m(\alpha_m)} e^{\alpha_m t} \right\}$

where $P(s) - (s - \alpha_1) \cdots (s - \alpha_n)$, $Q(s)$ is a polynomial of degree $n - 1$ at most, and $P_m(s) = P(s)/(s - \alpha_m)$.

2. Express

(i) $(s + \alpha)^{-n}$

(ii) $\dfrac{\lambda s + \mu}{(s + \alpha)^2 - \beta^2}$

(iii) $\dfrac{\lambda s^3 + \mu s^2 + \nu s + \beta}{(s^2 + \alpha^2)^2}$

as continuous functions of t.

3. Evaluate

$$\frac{\alpha s^2 + \beta}{s - 1} \{\sin \omega t\}.$$

3.3 Ordinary Linear Differential Equations with Constant Coefficients

We now have all the tools required for solving an ordinary linear differential equation with constant coefficients or a system of such equations.

In the case of a single equation,

$$\alpha_0 z^{(n)}(t) + \alpha_1 z^{(n-1)}(t) + \cdots + \alpha_{n-1} z'(t) + \alpha_n z(t) = f(t) \qquad (1)$$

we assume that $\alpha_0 \neq 0$, $\alpha_0, \cdots, \alpha_n \in \mathfrak{R}$, and that $f(t)$ is locally integrable so that $f = \{f(t)\} \in \mathfrak{R}$. The solution must possess a locally integrable derivative of order n so that theorem 7 applies, and

$$z^{(k)} = \{z^{(k)}(t)\} = s^k z - \sum_{j=1}^{k} z^{(k-j)}(0) s^{j-1} \qquad k = 1, 2, \cdots, n. \qquad (2)$$

Substituting (2) in (1), we set

$$P(s) = \sum_{k=0}^{n} \alpha_{n-k} s^k \tag{3}$$

$$Q(s) = \sum_{k=1}^{n} \sum_{j=1}^{k} \alpha_{n-k} z^{(k-j)}(0)\, s^{j-1} \tag{4}$$

and obtain

$$P(s)\, z = Q(s) + f \tag{5}$$

and hence

$$z = \frac{Q(s)}{P(s)} + \frac{f}{P(s)}. \tag{6}$$

Now, $P(s)$ is a polynomial of degree n in s and $Q(s)$, one of degree $n-1$ at most, so that $Q(s)/P(s) \, \epsilon \, \mathfrak{C}$ and is in fact a combination of polynomials in t multiplied by exponential functions. $Q(s)/P(s)$ can be evaluated by the methods developed in 3.2 thus giving the "complementary function." Similarly, $1/P(s) \, \epsilon \, \mathfrak{C}$ and can be evaluated, thus giving the "Green's function" of (1); and $f/P(s)$, being the convolution of two functions, is again a function.

If $z(0)$, $z'(0)$, $\cdots$, $z^{(n-1)}(0)$ are given, then $Q(s)$, and hence z, is uniquely determined. If initial conditions at a single point are given, shift the origin to this point and then apply (6). In the case of two-point boundary conditions, let the two points be $t = 0$ and $t = t_1 > 0$ and suppose that r conditions are prescribed at $t = 0$ and $n - r$ conditions at $t = t_1$. We then have r equations for the coefficients of $Q(s)$ so that $Q(s)$ will contain $n - r$ unknown parameters, these parameters will enter in the solution (6), and must be determined from the $n - r$ conditions at $t = t_1$.

EXAMPLE 1. To find that solution of the differential equation

$$z''(t) - 4z(t) = e^{2t} \tag{7}$$

which satisfies $z(0) = 1$, $z'(0) = \tfrac{1}{4}$.

By 3.1(3) and 3.2(1),

$$\{z''(t)\} = s^2\{z(t)\} - z'(0) - z(0)s = s^2 z - \tfrac{1}{4} - s, \qquad \{e^{2t}\} = \frac{1}{s-2}$$

so that our problem is equivalent to the algebraic equation

$$s^2 z - \tfrac{1}{4} - s - 4z = \frac{1}{s-2}$$

or

$$(s^2 - 4)\, z = \frac{1}{s-2} + \tfrac{1}{4} + s = \tfrac{1}{4}\frac{s+2}{s-2} + s$$

for the convolution quotient z (which will turn out to be a differentiable function).

We have

$$z = \frac{1}{4} \frac{1}{(s-2)^2} + \frac{s}{s^2-4}$$

and hence by 3.2(2) and 3.2 problem 1(i),

$$z(t) = \tfrac{1}{4} te^{2t} + \cosh 2t.$$

EXAMPLE 2. To find that solution of the differential equation

$$z''(t) + \alpha^2 z(t) = f(t) \qquad\qquad 0 \le t \le T \qquad (8)$$

which satisfies the boundary conditions

$$z(0) = z(T) = 0. \qquad (9)$$

Two complications arise in this problem. One arises from the circumstance that $f(t)$ is given, and $z(t)$ is to be determined, on the interval $0 \le t \le T$ only and the second, from a unique solution to our problem failing to exist for certain values of α. We shall see that the operational calculus developed here is able to cope with both of these complications.

We assume that $f(t)$ is given and absolutely integrable on the interval $0 \le t \le T$. This function can be continued in infinitely many ways so as to make it a locally integrable function on $(0, \infty)$ [for instance, we may put $f(t) = 0$ for $t > T$]. Let us denote by $f = \{f(t)\}$ any one of these continuations; it will turn out that the restriction of $z = \{z(t)\}$ to the interval $0 < t < T$ is independent of the particular continuation chosen.

We know that $z(0) = 0$ and we set $z'(0) = \beta$ for the time being. Then $\{z''(t)\} = s^2 z - \beta$, and (8) becomes $(s^2 + \alpha^2)z = \beta + f$ so that

$$z = \frac{\beta}{s^2 + \alpha^2} + \frac{f}{s^2 + \alpha^2} = \left\{\frac{\beta}{\alpha} \sin \alpha t\right\} + \left\{\frac{1}{\alpha} \sin \alpha t\right\} \{f(t)\}$$

by section 3.2, problem 1(i). Thus, for each $\beta \in \mathfrak{N}$,

$$z(t) = \frac{\beta}{\alpha} \sin \alpha t + \frac{1}{\alpha} \int_0^t \sin \alpha(t-u) f(u)\, du \qquad (10)$$

is a solution of (8) which satisfies the first condition (9). In order that $z(t)$ satisfy also the second condition (9), β must be a root of the equation

$$\frac{\beta}{\alpha} \sin \alpha T + \frac{1}{\alpha} \int_0^T \sin \alpha(T-u) f(u)\, du = 0 \qquad (11)$$

It is pertinent to point out that only those values of f for $0 \le t \le T$ enter into this equation.

From here on we must distinguish two cases. If $\sin \alpha\, T \neq 0$, then β is uniquely determined by (11), and the unique solution of our problem is

$$z(t) = \frac{1}{\alpha} \int_0^t \sin \alpha(t - u) f(u)\, du - \frac{1}{\alpha} \frac{\sin \alpha t}{\sin \alpha T} \int_0^T \sin \alpha(T - u) f(u)\, du.$$

Again it may be remarked that in case $0 \leq t \leq T$, only those values of f for $0 \leq t \leq T$ enter the solution. If $\sin \alpha T = 0$, then in general no $\beta \,\epsilon\, \mathfrak{R}$ will satisfy (11), and our problem will have no solution. However, if in this case $\int_0^T \sin \alpha(T - u) f(u)\, du = 0$ or, what is the same, $\int_0^T \sin \alpha u\, f(u)\, du = 0$, then every $\beta \,\epsilon\, \mathfrak{R}$ will satisfy (11), and for each $\beta \,\epsilon\, \mathfrak{R}$, (10) will represent a solution of (8), (9). Clearly, those values of α for which $\sin \alpha T = 0$ are the characteristic values of the homogeneous boundary value problem

$$z''(t) + \alpha^2 z(t) = 0, \qquad z(0) = z(T) = 0.$$

Systems of ordinary linear differential equations with constant coefficients may be solved by the same method. It will be sufficient to illustrate this by an example; and for the sake of comparison, we choose a system that has been solved by the Laplace transform method [Carslaw and Jaeger (1941) p. 15].

EXAMPLE 3. To solve

$$x'(t) - x(t) - 2y(t) = t, \qquad - 2x(t) + y'(t) - y(t) = t$$

given that $x(0) = 2$, $y(0) = 4$.

From 3.1(4), $x' = sx - 2$, $y' = sy - 4$, so that we have

$$sx - 2 - x - 2y = \{t\} = h^2 = \frac{1}{s^2}, \qquad - 2x + sy - 4 - y = \frac{1}{s^2}$$

or

$$(s - 1)\, x - 2y = 2 + \frac{1}{s^2}, \qquad - 2x + (s - 1)\, y = 4 + \frac{1}{s^2} \qquad (12)$$

Adding, we have $(s - 3)\, (x + y) = 6 + 2/s^2$, or

$$x + y = \frac{6}{s - 3} + \frac{2}{s^2(s - 3)} = \tfrac{5\,6}{9}\, \frac{1}{s - 3} - \tfrac{2}{9}\, \frac{s + 3}{s^2}$$

so that

$$x(t) + y(t) = \tfrac{5\,6}{9}\, e^{3t} - \tfrac{2}{9} - \tfrac{2}{3}\, t. \qquad (13)$$

Subtracting the equations (12), $(s + 1)\, (x - y) = - 2$, so that

$$x(t) - y(t) = - 2e^{-t}. \qquad (14)$$

From (13) and (14),

$$x(t) = \tfrac{28}{9} e^{3t} - e^{-t} - \tfrac{1}{9} - \tfrac{1}{3} t$$

$$y(t) = \tfrac{28}{9} e^{3t} + e^{-t} - \tfrac{1}{9} - \tfrac{1}{3} t.$$

PROBLEMS

Determine the functions which satisfy the given differential equations (systems) and initial conditions. (1 to 5).

1. $z''(t) - 2z'(t) + (1 + \alpha^2) z(t) = (1 + 4\alpha^2) \cos \alpha t, \quad z(0) = 1, \quad z'(0) = 0.$

2. $z'' + 3z'(t) + 2z(t) = 2te^{-t}, \quad z(1) = z'(1) = 0.$

3. $z^{(iv)}(t) - 2z''(t) + z(t) = 12te^{t}, \quad z(0) = z''(0) = \tfrac{1}{2}, \quad z'(0) = 0,$
$z'''(0) = -3.$

4. $7x'(t) + y'(t) + 2x(t) = \alpha \sin t$
$x'(t) + 3y'(t) + y(t) = 0$
$x(0) = y(0) - 0.$

5. $x''(t) + 3y'(t) - 4x(t) + 6y(t) = 10 \cos t$
$x'(t) + y''(t) - 2x(t) + 4y(t) - 0$
$x(0) = y(0) = 0, \quad x'(0) = 4, \quad y'(0) = 2.$

Discuss the solutions of the following boundary value problems. (6-8).

6. $z''(t) + \alpha^2 z(t) = 0, \quad z(0) = 0, \quad z'(T) = 1.$

7. $z''(t) + 2\beta z'(t) + \alpha^2 z(t) = f(t), \quad z'(0) = z'(T) = 0, \qquad$ where $\qquad f(t) = 2t$
when $0 \le t \le T/2$, and $= 2T - 2t$ when $T/2 \le t \le T.$

8. $x'(t) + y(t) = \sin 2t$
$y'(t) - x(t) = \cos 2t$
$x(\pi) = y(0) = 0.$

3.4 Integral Equations of the Convolution Type

Convolution quotients may also be used to solve certain integral equations. With f and k being given functions and z the function to be determined, the functional equation

$$\int_0^t k(t - u) z(u) \, du = f(t) \qquad\qquad t \ge 0 \qquad (1)$$

is called an *integral equation of the first kind*, and

$$z(t) + \int_0^t k(t - u) z(u) \, du = f(t) \qquad\qquad t \ge 0 \qquad (2)$$

an *integral equation of the second kind* of the convolution type. k is called the *kernel* of the integral equation.

We write (1) and (2) as $kz = f$ and $z + kz = f$, respectively, and obtain the solutions as $z = f/k$ and $z = f/(1 + k)$, respectively, in the form of convolution quotients. Now, we shall see in section 4.2 that $m = (1 + k)^{-1} - 1$ is a continuous function if k is a continuous function (and, according to section 4.2, example 1 is a locally integrable function whenever k is locally integrable), so that $f/(1 + k) = f + mf$ is always a locally integrable function if f is locally integrable and k is continuous (or locally integrable). Thus, under very liberal assumptions, the solution of (2) exists as a (locally integrable) function; and this solution is unique. Against this, f/k may fail to be a function even if f and k are continuous functions, so that (1), although it always possesses a solution that is a convolution quotient, may fail to possess a solution that is a function. However, the solution of (1), whether a function or a convolution quotient, is unique.

It will be sufficient to illustrate the points arising in the solution of integral equations by a few examples.

EXAMPLE 1. To solve

$$\int_0^t \sin\,(t - u)\,z(u)\,du = \alpha t + \beta t^2 \qquad\qquad t \geq 0$$

By section 3.2, problem 1(i), $\{\sin t\} = (s^2 + 1)^{-1}$ so that the integral equation may be written as $(s^2 + 1)^{-1}\,z = \alpha h^2 + 2\beta\,h^3$, and the solution, as

$$z = (s^2 + 1)\,(\alpha h^2 + 2\beta h^3) = 2\beta h^3 + \alpha h^2 + 2\beta h + \alpha = \{\beta t^2 + \alpha t + 2\beta\} + \alpha.$$

Thus, the solution of the integral equation is a (continuous) function' $z(t) = \beta t^2 + 2\beta$, if and only if $\alpha = 0$. If $\alpha \neq 0$, the solution is a generalized function—namely, a sum of a continuous function and of a numerical multiple of the delta function.

EXAMPLE 2. To solve

$$z(t) = \alpha t + \int_0^t \sin\,(t - u)\,z(u)\,du \qquad\qquad t \geq 0.$$

In this case $z = \alpha h^2 + (s^2 + 1)^{-1}\,z$, or

$$z = \frac{\alpha h^2}{1 - (s^2 + 1)^{-1}} = \frac{\alpha h^2 (s^2 + 1)}{s^2} = \alpha(h^4 + h^2)$$

so that the solution is the continuous function for which $z(t) = \alpha[(t^3/3!) + t]$.

EXAMPLE 3. Let $J_n(z)$ denote the Bessel function of the first kind of order n. We shall see in section 4.2, examples 2 and 3, that the operators $(s^2 + 1)^{\pm 1/2}$ can be defined, and furthermore that

$$(s^2 + 1)^{1/2} = s + \left\{\frac{J_1(t)}{t}\right\}, \qquad (s^2 + 1)^{-1/2} = \{J_0(t)\}.$$

Anticipating these results, let us solve the integral equation

$$\int_0^t J_0(t - u)\, z(u)\, du = f(t) \qquad\qquad t \geq 0$$

in which f is a given locally integrable function.

We have $(s^2 + 1)^{-1/2}\, z = f$ and hence

$$z = (s^2 + 1)^{1/2} f = \left\{ \frac{J_1(t)}{t} \right\} f + sf.$$

The first term on the right is always a function but the second term in general is not. For the solution of the integral equation to be a locally integrable function it is both necessary and sufficient that f possess a locally integrable derivative, and that $f(0) = 0$. If these conditions are satisfied, equation 3.1(4) can be used to show that the solution of the integral equation is given by

$$z(t) = \int_0^t \frac{J_1(t - u)}{t - u} f(u)\, du + f'(t).$$

The same technique can be used to solve systems of integral equations, integro-differential equations, and some nonlinear integral equations. Reference: Butzer (1958).

EXAMPLE 4. To solve

$$z(t) = \sin t + 2 \int^t \sin (t - u)\, z'(u)\, du \qquad\qquad t \geq 0.$$

Here $z(0) = 0$ from the integral equation and hence $z' = sz$. The integral equation may be transcribed as $z = (s^2 + 1)^{-1} + 2(s^2 + 1)^{-1} sz$. Solving this, $z = (s - 1)^{-2} = \{te^t\}$.

PROBLEMS

Solve the following functional equations, supposed to hold for $t \geq 0$.

1. $z(t) + 2 \int_0^t \cos (t - u)\, z(u)\, du = e^{t^2}.$

2. $z(t) - (1 - t)e^t = \int_0^t z(t - u)\, z(u)\, du.$

3. $z(t) = \alpha \cos \omega t + \beta \int_0^t \sin \omega(t - u)\, z(u)\, du.$

4. $z(t) = \alpha \cos \omega t + \beta \int_0^t \cos \omega(t - u)\, z'(u)\, du.$

5. $z(t) = \alpha t^n + \beta \int_0^t (t - u)^{-1/2}\, z(u)\, du.$

6. Show that under certain conditions, the integral equation

$$\int_0^\xi (\xi^2 - \eta^2)^{\alpha-1}\, \chi(\eta)\, d\eta = \phi(\xi) \qquad\qquad \xi \geq 0$$

possesses the (unique solution)

$$\chi(\xi) = \frac{2}{\pi} \sin \alpha\pi \left[\phi(0)\, \xi^{1-2\alpha} + \xi \int_0^\xi (\xi^2 - \eta^2)^{-\alpha}\, \phi'(\eta)\, d\eta \right]$$

and formulate a set of such conditions.

[4]

Convergence of Convolution Quotients.
Operator Functions

4.1 Sequences of Convolution Quotients

First we shall consider sequences of continuous functions. For these the appropriate notion of convergence is that of uniform convergence on each finite interval. For the sake of brevity, this will be called uniform convergence simply.

DEFINITION 7. A sequence of functions, $f_n(t)$, defined for $t \geq 0$, is said to converge *uniformly* if for each $\epsilon > 0$ and each $T > 0$ there is an integer $n_0 = n_0(\epsilon, T)$ so that $|f_m(t) - f_n(t)| < \epsilon$ whenever $m > n_0$, $n > n_0$ and $0 \leq t \leq T$.

Clearly, this notion of convergence demands more than convergence for each fixed $t \geq 0$ but it demands less than uniform convergence for all $t \geq 0$. For instance, $\exp(t^2/n) \to 1$ as $n \to \infty$ uniformly on each finite interval but not uniformly for all $t \geq 0$.

It is known that the limit of a uniformly convergent sequence of continuous functions is itself continuous. We shall now show that uniform convergence is preserved under convolution.

LEMMA 5. If $f_n \in \mathfrak{C}$ for $n = 1, 2, \cdots, f_n \to f$ uniformly as $n \to \infty$, and $c \in \mathfrak{C}$, then $cf_n \to cf$ uniformly as $n \to \infty$.

Proof. Fix $\epsilon > 0$ and $T > 0$, and let $0 \leq t \leq T$. Then $|c(t)| \leq M$ for some M, and there is an integer $n_0 = n_0(\epsilon, T)$ so that $|f_n(t) - f(t)| < \epsilon$ when $n > n_0$ and $0 \leq t \leq T$. Consequently,

$$|cf_n(t) - cf(t)|$$

$$= \left| \int_0^t c(t-u)[f_n(u) - f(u)]\, du \right| \leq \int_0^t |c(t-u)|\, |f_n(u) - f(u)|\, du < M\epsilon T,$$

and since $M\epsilon T$ can be made arbitrarily small by choosing ϵ sufficiently small, this proves the lemma.

Next we turn to sequences in $\mathfrak{F}$. We shall define convergence for those sequences of convolution quotients which have a common denominator, calling such a sequence convergent if the sequence of numerators (which are continuous functions) is convergent in the sense of definition 7.

DEFINITION 8. A sequence of convolution quotients, a_n, is said to be *convergent* if there exists a, $p \in \mathfrak{F}$ such that $p \neq 0$, and pa_n, $n = 1, 2, \cdots$, is a uniformly convergent sequence of continuous functions.

In such a case we set $a = p^{-1} \{\lim pa_n(t)\}$, call a the *limit* of the sequence $a_1, a_2, \cdots$, and write $a = \lim a_n$ or $a_n \to a$ as $n \to \infty$. The qualifying phrase "as $n \to \infty$" will frequently be omitted.

Clearly, for sequences of numbers, convergence in the sense of this definition and convergence in the ordinary sense are equivalent notions. The examples to be given below show that, for sequences of functions, convergence in the sense of definition 8 demands less, while uniform convergence in the sense of definition 7 demands more, than pointwise convergence.

If $p = b/c$ is the convolution quotient occurring in definition 8, where $b \in \mathfrak{C}$ and $c \in \mathfrak{C}$, then $(b/c) a_n \to (b/c)a$ uniformly. It follows from lemma 5 that then also $ba_n \to ba$ uniformly, thus showing that we may always take $p \in \mathfrak{C}$. We shall frequently make use of this remark.

The principal properties of convergence in $\mathfrak{F}$ are summarized in the following theorem in which a, b, a_n, $b_n \in \mathfrak{F}$.

THEOREM 8. (i) $\lim a_n$, if it exists, is unique. (ii) If $a_n = a$ for $n = 1, 2, \cdots$, then $\lim a_n = a$. (iii) If $\lim a_n = a$ and $\lim b_n = b$ then $\lim (a_n + b_n) = a + b$, (iv) Under the hypotheses of (iii) $\lim a_n b_n = ab$.

Proof. (i) Suppose that $p^{-1} \{\lim pa_n(t)\} = a$, $q^{-1} \{\lim qa_n(t)\} = b$. Then $pa_n \to pa$ and $qa_n \to qb$ uniformly, and by lemma 5, $qpa_n \to qpa$ and $pqa_n \to pqb$ uniformly. Thus $qpa = pqb$, and $a = b$ by theorem 2. The proof of (ii) is immediate. The proof of (iii) follows from the remark that in the event that $pa_n \to pa$ and $qb_n \to qb$ uniformly, it follows from lemma 5 that $pqa_n \to pqa$ and $pqb_n \to pqb$ uniformly, and hence $pq(a_n + b_n) \to pq(a + b)$ uniformly. (iv) Fix $\epsilon > 0$ and $T > 0$, and let $0 \leq t \leq T$. Since a uniformly convergent sequence of bounded functions is uniformly bounded, there exists an $M > 0$ so that $|pa_n(t)| < M$ and $|qb(t)| < M$ for $n = 1, 2, \cdots$, and there exists an $n_0 = n_0(T, \epsilon)$ so that

$$|pa_n(t) - pa(t)| < \frac{\epsilon}{2MT}, \qquad |qb_n(t) - qb(t)| < \frac{\epsilon}{2MT} \qquad \text{for} \qquad n > n_0.$$

Then

$$|pqa_nb_n(t) - pqab(t)| = \left| \int_0^t [pa_n(t - u) qb_n(u) - pa(t - u) qb(u)] \, du \right|$$

$$\leq \int_0^t |pa_n(t - u)| \, |qb_n(u) - qb(u)| \, du$$

$$+ \int_0^t |pa_n(t - u) - pa(t - u)| \, |qb(u)| \, du$$

$$< M \frac{\epsilon}{2MT} T + \frac{\epsilon}{2MT} MT = \epsilon \qquad \text{for} \qquad n > n_0$$

so that $pqa_nb_n \to pqab$ uniformly.

We shall now give a few examples that will illustrate some properties of the convergence theory outlined here.

EXAMPLE 1. To show that $c^n \to 0$ uniformly if $c \in \mathfrak{C}$.

Choose $T > 0$ and let $0 \leq t \leq T$. Then $|c(t)| \leq M$ for some $M > 0$ on this interval, and we shall show by induction that

$$|c^n(t)| \leq \frac{M^n t^{n-1}}{(n-1)!} \qquad \text{for} \qquad n = 1, 2, \cdots. \tag{1}$$

Now, (1) certainly holds when $n = 1$. Suppose it holds for n. Then

$$|c^{n+1}(t)| = \left| \int_0^t c(t-u)\, c^n(u)\, du \right| < \int_0^t M \frac{M^n u^{n-1}}{(n-1)!}\, du = \frac{M^{n+1} t^n}{n!}$$

and (1) holds also for $n + 1$. Since the right-hand side of (1) approaches zero, uniformly for $0 \leq t \leq T$, as $n \to \infty$, we have the desired result.

EXAMPLE 2. To prove that $\{\sin nt\} \to 0$. The proof follows from

$$h\{\sin nt\} = \left\{ \int_0^t \sin nu\, du \right\} = \left\{ \frac{1 - \cos nt}{n} \right\} \to 0 = h\{0\}$$

uniformly (in this case for all $t \geq 0$).

This example shows that a sequence of functions may converge in the sense of definition 8 even though it fails to converge pointwise. The next example shows that in the case of such a generalized convergence the limit may be a generalized function.

EXAMPLE 3. To prove that

$$\left\{ n f(nt) \Big/ \int_0^\infty f(u)\, du \right\} \to 1 \tag{2}$$

provided that f is locally integrable, $\int_0^\infty |f(u)|\, du$ is convergent, and

$$\int_0^\infty f(u)\, du \neq 0.$$

This result may be interpreted as describing approximations to the delta function (which corresponds to 1) in terms of locally integrable functions. Most familiar approximations to the delta function [see van der Pol and Bremmer (1950) Chapter V] are special cases of (2).

To prove (2), we replace $f(u)$ by a suitable constant multiple so as to make $\int_0^\infty f(u)\, du = 1$, and set $\int_0^\infty |f(u)|\, du = A$. Now $\{nf(nt)\}$ is integrable, and $h\{nf(nt)\} = \{\int_0^{nt} f(v)\, dv\}$ is continuous and approaches $\{1\} = h$ as $n \to \infty$, for all $t > 0$. The convergence is not uniform, however, and we shall take $p = h^2$ in definition 8.

$$h^2\{nf(nt)\} = h\left\{\int_0^{nt} f(v)\,dv\right\} = \left\{\int_0^t du \int_0^{nu} f(v)\,dv\right\}.$$

We set

$$\phi_n(t) = t - \int_0^t du \int_0^{nu} f(v)\,dv = \int_0^t \left[1 - \int_0^{nu} f(v)\,dv\right] du = \int_0^t du \int_{nu}^{\infty} f(v)\,dv.$$

Clearly, ϕ_n is continuous. We shall establish (2) by showing that $\phi_n \to 0$ uniformly.

Fix $T > 0$, let $0 \le t \le T$, and let δ be any number, to be chosen later, between 0 and T. If $0 \le t \le \delta$, we have

$$|\phi_n(t)| \le \int_0^\delta du \int_0^\infty |f(v)|\,dv = \delta A,$$

and if $\delta \le t \le T$, we have

$$|\phi_n(t)| \le \int_0^\delta du \int_0^\infty |f(v)|\,dv + \int_\delta^t du \int_{n\delta}^\infty |f(v)|\,dv \le \delta A + T \int_{n\delta}^\infty |f(v)|\,dv,$$

so that the latter estimate holds for all δ, $0 < \delta < T$ and all t, $0 \le t \le T$. Given $\epsilon > 0$, we first choose $\delta \le \epsilon/(2A)$. Having fixed δ, $\int_{n\delta}^\infty |f(v)|\,dv \to 0$ as $n \to \infty$, and we may choose n_0 so that $\int_{n_0\delta}^\infty |f(v)|\,dv < \epsilon/(2T)$. We then have $|\phi_n(t)| < \epsilon$ for $0 \le t \le T$ and $n > n_0$, thus establishing (2).

EXAMPLE 4. We have seen in example 1 that $c^n \to 0$ uniformly if $c \in \mathfrak{C}$. It can be proved [see Mikusiński (1959) p. 370 f.] that $f^n \to 0$, indeed $hf^n \to 0$ uniformly, for all $f \in \mathfrak{R}$. Although we shall not establish this result in its full generality, we shall prove it for a class of locally integrable functions which is large enough to contain most functions the reader is likely to encounter.

We first prove an estimate which corresponds to (1) and holds for all $f \in \mathfrak{R}$. We know that $g(t) = \int_0^t |f(u)|\,du \to 0$ as $t \to 0$. Let us assume* that $\int_0^t |f(u)\,du = O(t^\alpha)$ as $t \to 0$, where $\alpha \ge 0$. Fix $T > 0$ and let $0 \le t \le T$. Then $t^{-\alpha} g(t)$ is continuous for $0 < t \le T$ and bounded in some neighborhood of $t = 0$ so that it is bounded for $0 < t \le T$. Say

$$0 \le \int_0^t |f(u)|\,du \le \frac{At^\alpha}{\Gamma(\alpha + 1)} \qquad 0 \le t \le T \qquad (3)$$

We shall prove by induction that

$$|hf^n(t)| \le \frac{A^n\,t^{n\alpha}}{\Gamma(n\alpha + 1)} \qquad \text{for} \qquad n = 1, 2, \cdots \qquad \text{and} \qquad 0 \le t \le T. \qquad (4)$$

(*) We say that $F(x) = O[G(x)]$ as $x \to x_0$ if $F(x)/G(x)$ is bounded in some neighborhood of x_0.

This estimate clearly holds for $n = 1$. Suppose it holds for some n. Then

$$|hf^{n+1}(t)| = \left| \int_0^t hf^n(t-u) f(u)\, du \right| \leq \int_0^t |hf^n(t-u)|\, |f(u)|\, du$$

$$\leq \frac{A^n}{\Gamma(n\alpha + 1)} \int_0^t (t-u)^{n\alpha}\, g'(u)\, du$$

Integrating by parts we obtain

$$\frac{A^n}{\Gamma(n\alpha + 1)} \int_0^t (t-u)^{n\alpha}\, g'(u)\, du = \frac{A^n n\alpha}{\Gamma(n\alpha + 1)} \int_0^t (t-u)^{n\alpha-1}\, g(u)\, du$$

$$\leq \frac{A^{n+1}}{\Gamma(n\alpha)\, \Gamma(\alpha+1)} \int_0^t (t-u)^{n\alpha-1}\, u^\alpha\, du = \frac{A^{n+1} t^{n\alpha+\alpha}}{\Gamma(n\alpha + \alpha + 1)}$$

by Euler's integral of the first kind so that (4) holds also for $n + 1$ and hence generally.

It follows from (4) that $hf^n \to 0$ uniformly, and hence $f \to 0$, provided that $f \in \Re$ and $\int_0^t |f(u)|\, du = O(t^\alpha)$ as $t \to 0$ for some $\alpha > 0$.

PROBLEMS

1. Verify that $\{t/(t + n)\} \to 0$ and $\{t \arctan nt\} \to \{\frac{1}{2}\pi t\}$ uniformly. Does $\{\arctan nt\}$ have a uniform limit?

2 Show that

$$\{\arctan nt\} \to \tfrac{1}{2}\pi h, \qquad \{ne^{-nt}\} \to 1, \qquad \left\{ \frac{2}{\pi} \frac{n}{1 + n^2 t^2} \right\} \to 1.$$

Use example 3 to construct some approximations to the delta function.

3. Find conditions on $\alpha_n \in \Re$ which will ensure that $\alpha_n f^n \to 0$ for all $f \in \Re$. [Hint: Use (4) with $\alpha = 0$]

4. Suppose that $f(t)$ and $|f(t)|^2$ are both locally integrable and $\int_0^T |f(u)|\, du \leq M$, $\int_0^T |f(u)|^2\, du \leq M$. Show that

$$|f^{2n}(t)| \leq \frac{M^n t^{n-1}}{(n-1)!}, \qquad |f^{2n+1}(t)| \leq \frac{M^{n+1} t^{n-1}}{(n-1)!} \qquad n = 1, 2, \cdots, \qquad 0 \leq t \leq T.$$

Deduce that $hf^n \to 0$ uniformly in this case. [Butzer (1958).]

5. If $f(t)$ and $|f(t)|^2$ are both locally integrable, show that $\int_0^t |f(u)|\, du = O(t^{1/2})$ as $t \to 0$ and deduce that $hf^n \to 0$ uniformly. [Hint: Use Schwarz's inequality.]

6. If $f(t)$ is locally integrable and $f(t) = O(t^{\alpha-1})$ as $t \to 0$ for some $\alpha > 0$, show that $\int_0^t |f(u)|\, du = O(t^\alpha)$ as $t \to 0$, and deduce that $hf^n \to 0$ uniformly.

7. Let $a_n = 1 - s/n$. Show that $a_n \to 1$ but a_n^{-1} does not converge as $n \to \infty$. (This example shows that convolution division is not a continuous operation.) [Mikusiński (1959) p. 147 f.]

4.2 Infinite Series of Convolution Quotients

DEFINITION 9. $\Sigma\, a_n$ is said to be convergent if the sequence of partial sums $a_0 + a_1 + \cdots + a_n$ is convergent. For a convergent series we set

$$\sum_{n=0}^{\infty} a_n = \lim (a_0 + \cdots + a_n)$$

as $n \to \infty$.

For a series of numbers, or numerical operators, this notion of convergence is equivalent to ordinary convergence.

THEOREM 9. (i) $\Sigma\, a_n$ is convergent if and only if there exists a $p \neq 0$ so that $\Sigma\, pa_n$ is a uniformly convergent series of continuous functions. p itself may be taken as a continuous function, and $\Sigma\, a_n = p^{-1} \{\Sigma\, pa_n(t)\}$. (ii) If $\Sigma\, a_n$ is convergent then $a_n \to 0$ as $n \to \infty$. (iii) If $\Sigma\, a_n = a$, $\Sigma\, b_n = b$, and c and d are any convolution quotients, then $\Sigma\, (ca_n + db_n)$ is convergent and $\Sigma\, (ca_n + db_n) = ca + db$.

These statements are immediate consequences of the properties of convergence in $\mathfrak{F}$: their proof is left as an exercise.

Many of the infinite series occurring in operational calculus are *power series*, in particular power series with numerical coefficients, $\Sigma\, \alpha_n w^n$, where $\alpha_n \in \mathfrak{N}$, $w \in \mathfrak{F}$, and $w^0 = 1$ by definition. The convergence of such power series can often be deduced from the convergence of an associated power series in powers of a numerical variable. We shall establish a few results of this nature. It will be seen from the proof of these results that the p appearing in these cases is either 1 or h so that in all cases $\Sigma\, \alpha_n h w^n$ is a uniformly convergent series of continuous functions.

DEFINITION 10. For $\alpha > 0$, let $\mathfrak{R}_\alpha$ be the collection of equivalence classes of those locally integrable functions with the property that $\int_0^t |f(u)|\, du = O(t^\alpha)$ as $t \to 0$.

Clearly, each $\mathfrak{R}_\alpha$ is a subset of $\mathfrak{R}$, and $\mathfrak{R}_\alpha$ decreases as α increases. Estimates of the form 4.1(4) hold for $f \in \mathfrak{R}_\alpha$.

THEOREM 10. (i) If $\Sigma\, \alpha_n \zeta^n$ is convergent for all $\zeta \in \mathfrak{N}$, then $\Sigma\, \alpha_n f^n$ is convergent for all $f \in \mathfrak{R}$. (ii) If $\alpha > 0$, and $\Sigma\, \alpha_n \zeta^n / \Gamma(n\alpha + 1)$ is convergent for all ζ, then $\Sigma\, \alpha_n f^n$ is convergent for $f \in \mathfrak{R}_\alpha$.

COROLLARY. (i) If $\Sigma\, \alpha_n \zeta^n / n!$ is convergent for all $\zeta \in \mathfrak{N}$ and $c \in \mathfrak{C}$, then $\Sigma_{n=1}^{\infty} \alpha_n c^n$ is a uniformly convergent series of continuous functions. (ii) If the sequence of coefficients α_n is bounded, and $c \in \mathfrak{C}$, then $\Sigma_{n=1}^{\infty} \alpha_n c^n$ is a uniformly convergent series of continuous functions. In this case $\Sigma\, \alpha_n f^n$ converges for all those $f \in \mathfrak{R}_\alpha$ for some $\alpha > 0$.

Proof. (i) Fixing T and letting $0 \leq t \leq T$, we obtain $|hf^n(t)| \leq A^n$ from 4.1(4) with $\alpha = 0$. Thus, $\Sigma \, \alpha_n hf^n$ is a uniformly convergent series of continuous functions by comparison with $\Sigma \, |\alpha_n| A^n$. (ii) Here we use equation 4.1(4) similarly to show that $\Sigma \, \alpha_n hf^n(t)$ is dominated, on the interval $0 \leq t \leq T$, by

$$\Sigma \, \frac{|\alpha_n| \, (AT^\alpha)^n}{\Gamma(n\alpha + 1)} \, .$$

Proof of the corollary. (i) Here we use equation 4.1(1). (ii) If the α_n are bounded and α is any positive number, then $\Sigma \, \alpha_n \zeta^n / \Gamma(n\alpha + 1)$ converges for all $\zeta \, \epsilon \, \mathfrak{R}$, and Part (ii) of the theorem applies.

EXAMPLE 1. To investigate the convergence of $\Sigma \, w^n$. By corollary (ii) above, this series certainly converges when $w \, \epsilon \, \mathfrak{R}_\alpha$ for some $\alpha > 0$, and $\Sigma_{n=1}^\infty c^n$, with $c \, \epsilon \, \mathfrak{C}$, is a uniformly convergent series of continuous functions. We shall now show that $\Sigma \, w^n$ converges, and $\Sigma_{n=0}^\infty w^n = (1 - w)^{-1}$, if and only if $w^n \to 0$ as $n \to \infty$.

The series clearly fails to converge if $w = 1$. Assuming $w \neq 1$,

$$(1 - w) \, (1 + w + \cdots + w^n) = 1 - w^{n+1}$$

and for the convergence of $\Sigma \, w^n$ it is necessary and sufficient that $\lim w^n$ exist. Let $\lim w^n = a$. Then $aw = a$, since $\lim w^{n+1} = \lim w^n$, and a must be 0, since $w - 1 \neq 0$. This proves the statement.

If $f \, \epsilon \, \mathfrak{R}$ then $f^n \to 0$ (see section 4.1, example 4) and hence

$$\sum_{n=0}^{\infty} f^n = (1 - f)^{-1}$$

in this case. Moreover, it can be proved that in this case

$$\sum_{n=1}^{\infty} f^n = (1 - f)^{-1} - 1$$

is locally integrable, at least in the sense of the Lebesgue theory [see Mikusiński (1959) p. 370], a result which is of importance in connection with integral equations (see sec. 3.4).

EXAMPLE 2. To show that for $\gamma \, \epsilon \, \mathfrak{R}$

$$r = \sum_{n=0}^{\infty} \binom{1/2}{n} \gamma^{2n} h^{2n-1} \tag{1}$$

converges, $r - s \, \epsilon \, \mathfrak{C}$, and $r^2 = s^2 + \gamma^2$.

Since $|\binom{1/2}{n}| \leq 1$ and $\gamma^2 h^2 \ \epsilon \ \mathfrak{C}$, it follows from corollary (ii) that the infinite series for $hr - 1$ is uniformly convergent. By direct computation

$$r - s = \left\{ \sum_{n=1}^{\infty} \frac{(-1)^{n-1} \gamma^{2n} t^{2n-2}}{2^{2n-1}(n-1)! n!} \right\} \ \epsilon \ \mathfrak{C}$$

since the infinite series on the right converges uniformly on every finite interval. Lastly,

$$r^2 - s^2 = 2s(r - s) + (r - s)^2.$$

The infinite series for $r - s$ is a power series in t and may be differentiated term by term, $(r - s)^2$ may be formed similarly, and on carrying through the computations, one obtains $r^2 - s^2 = \gamma^2$.

We shall use r as the definition of $\sqrt{s^2 + \gamma^2}$.

EXAMPLE 3. To prove that

$$(r - s)^n = \left\{ \frac{n\gamma^n}{t} J_n(\gamma t) \right\} \qquad n = 1, 2, 3, \cdots \qquad (2)$$

$$r^{-1}(r - s)^n = \left\{ \gamma^n J_n(\gamma t) \right\} \qquad n = 0, 1, 2, \cdots \qquad (3)$$

where r is given by (1), and

$$J_n(z) = \sum_{m=0}^{\infty} \frac{(-1)^m z^{2m+n}}{2^{2m+n} m!(m + n)!} \qquad (4)$$

is the Bessel function of the first kind of order n.

The proof will be based on the hypergeometric expansions

$$f_n(z) = (\sqrt{1 + z} - 1)^n = n \sum_{m=0}^{\infty} \frac{(-1)^m (2m + n - 1)! \, z^{m+n}}{2^{2m+n} m!(m + n)!} \qquad n = 1, 2, 3, \cdots$$

$$g_n(z) = \frac{(\sqrt{1 + z} - 1)^n}{\sqrt{1 + z}} = \sum_{m=0}^{\infty} \frac{(-1)^m (2m + n)! \, z^{m+n}}{2^{2m+n} m!(m + n)!} \qquad n = 0, 1, 2, \cdots$$

which we shall prove by induction.

The expansions of f_1, g_0, and g_1 may be verified by means of the binomial theorem. Moreover,

$$f_n(z) - g_n(z) = g_{n+1}(z), \qquad z g_n(z) - g_{n+1}(z) = f_{n+1}(z).$$

Assuming that the above expansions hold for f_n and g_n, it can be verified from the recurrence relations that they also hold for g_{n+1} and f_{n+1}; thus they hold for all n.

We now form $s^n f_n (\gamma^2 h^2)$ and $s^{n-1} g_n (\gamma^2 h^2)$, find that the resulting series are convergent by theorem 10, and hence verify (2) and (3).

PROBLEMS

1. Investigate the convergence of the series

(i) $\displaystyle\sum \frac{1}{n + \alpha s}$, (ii) $\displaystyle\sum \frac{1}{n(n + \alpha s)}$, (iii) $\displaystyle\sum \frac{1}{n^2 + \alpha^2 s^2}$.

2. Prove theorem 9.

3. If $\Sigma \alpha_n$ is an absolutely convergent series of complex numbers, and $a_n \to a$, prove that $\Sigma \alpha_n a_n$ is convergent.

4. Prove that $\Sigma_{n=0}^{\infty} f^n/n!$ is convergent, and $\Sigma hf^n/n!$ is uniformly convergent, if $f \in \mathfrak{R}$. Denoting the sum of the first of these series by $g(f)$, prove that $g(f_1 + f_2) = g(f_1) g(f_2)$.

5. Discuss the convergence of the series $\Sigma_{n=0}^{\infty} \binom{v}{n} f^n$ (i) when $f \in \mathfrak{C}$, (ii) when $f \in \mathfrak{R}_\alpha$ for some $\alpha > 0$, (iii) when $f \in \mathfrak{R}$. Denoting the sum of this series, when convergent, by $g(f, v)$, show that $g(f, m) = (1 + f)^m$ when m is an integer, and show also that

$$g(f, v_1) g(f, v_2) = g(f, v_1 + v_2)$$

6. Prove that $\Sigma \alpha_n f^n$ is convergent under any of the following three sets of conditions: (i) $\alpha > 0$, $\Sigma \alpha_n \zeta^n / \Gamma(n\alpha + 1)$ convergent for all $\zeta \in \mathfrak{N}$, $f \in \mathfrak{R}$, $f(t) = O(t^{\alpha-1})$ as $t \to 0$; (ii) $\delta > 0$, $|\alpha_n n^{n\delta}| \leq A$, $n = 1, 2, \cdots$, $f \in \mathfrak{R}$; (iii) $\alpha > 0$, $\alpha + \delta > 0$, $|\alpha_n n^{n\delta}| \leq A$, $n = 1, 2, \cdots$, $f \in \mathfrak{R}$, $f(t) = O(t^{\alpha-1})$ as $t \to 0$. Compare these results with theorem 10 and its corollary.

7. Discuss the convergence of series of the form $\Sigma c_n \zeta^n$, where $c_n \in \mathfrak{C}$ and $\zeta \in \mathfrak{N}$. For a given set of coefficients c_n investigate the region of convergence in the ζ plane. Is it legitimate to form the Cauchy product of such series?

4.3 Operator Functions

Operator functions may depend on variables of any nature. Here we shall restrict ourselves to operator functions of a *single real variable* x ranging over an interval I which may be finite or infinite, open, half-open, or closed. The phrase "all x" will refer to the interval $-\infty < x < \infty$, "all $x \geq x_0$" to the interval $x_0 \leq x < \infty$, etc.

DEFINITION 11. (i) ϕ or $\phi(x)$ is called a *numerical function* on I if for each x in I, $\phi(x)$ is defined, and is a real or complex number. (ii) $a(x)$ is called an *operator function* on I if for each x in I, $a(x)$ is defined and is a convolution quotient.

A function $f(x, t)$ that is defined in the domain $D = D_I: x \in I$, $t \geq 0$ and that, for every fixed x in I, is a continuous function of t, defines an operator function $f(x) = \{f(x, t)\}$ on I. All operator functions that we shall encounter are related to these special operator functions and this circumstance will enable us to use simple notions of limits, continuity, etc. The corresponding notions for numerical functions are assumed to be known from analysis.

DEFINITION 12. (i) We say that $a(x) \to a$ as $x \to x_0$ if x_0 is a limit point of I and $a(x_n) \to a$ as $n \to \infty$ whenever $x_n \in I$ for all n and $x_n \to x_0$ as $n \to \infty$. (ii) The operator function $a(x)$ on I is called *continuous*, $a(x) \in C$, if corresponding to each finite closed subinterval J of I there is a $p = p_J \in \mathfrak{F}$ so that $p \neq 0$ and $pa(x)$ is a continuous function of x and t in D_J.

If I itself is a finite closed interval, we may take $J = I$ in (ii). In other cases there may not be a single p that will make $pa(x)$ continuous in D_I.

If $pa(x)$ is a continuous function of x and t, and $q \in \mathfrak{C}$, then $pqa(x)$ is also a continuous function of x and t. It follows that we may take $p \in \mathfrak{C}$ in definition 12 (ii).

If it is desirable to indicate that the values of a function lie in $\mathfrak{F}$, $\mathfrak{C}$, or $\mathfrak{N}$, we write $C\mathfrak{F}$, $C\mathfrak{C}$, $C\mathfrak{N}$; and if it is desirable to indicate the domain, we write $C(I)$, $C\mathfrak{F}(I)$, etc.

THEOREM 11. (i) If $a(x) = a$ for all $x \in I$, then $a(x) \in C$. (ii) If $a(x) \in C(I)$ and $x_0 \in I$, then $a(x) \to a(x_0)$ as $x \to x_0$. (iii) If $\phi(x) \in C\mathfrak{N}$ and $a(x)$, $b(x) \in C\mathfrak{F}$, then $a(x) + b(x)$, $\phi(x) a(x)$, $a(x)b(x) \in C\mathfrak{F}$.

Proof. (i) is obvious. (ii) For each finite closed interval J in I there exists a $p \neq 0$ so that $pa(x)$ is continuous in D_J and hence uniformly continuous when $x \in J$ and $0 \leq t \leq T$ for any (fixed) T. Given $\epsilon > 0$, there exists a $\delta = \delta(J, T, \epsilon) > 0$ so that $|pa (x, t) - pa(x_0, t)| < \epsilon$ when $x, x_0 \in J$, $|x - x_0| < \delta$, and $0 \leq t \leq T$. This proves that $a(x) \to a(x_0)$ as $x \to x_0$. (iii) The first two statements are obvious, the proof of the third statement follows from the remark that the continuity of $pa(x, t)$ and $qb(x, t)$ in D_J entails that of

$$pq \, ab(x, t) = \int_0^t pa(x, t - u) \, qb(x, u) \, du.$$

EXAMPLE 1. $\{\cos (x - t)\} \in C\mathfrak{C}$ for all x. By section 3.2, problem 6 (i),

$$\{\cos (x - t)\} = \frac{s \cos x + \sin x}{s^2 + 1}.$$

EXAMPLE 2. h^x, defined for all x at the beginning of section 3.1, is continuous for all x. To see this, let J be any finite closed interval and n a nonnegative integer such that $n + x > 1$ for all $x \in J$. Then $h^n h^x = \{t^{x+n-1}/\Gamma(n + x)\}$ is continuous in D_J. The continuity of h^x together with the properties of this function established in sections 2.1 and 3.1 justify the definition given in 2.1(3).

EXAMPLE 3. For $x \geq 0$ set $h_1(x, t) = 0$ if $0 \leq t < x$, $= 1$ if $x \leq t < \infty$. $h_1(x) = \{h_1(x, t)\}$ is Heaviside's unit function "shifted by x," and $h_1(0) = h$. For all $\alpha \in \mathfrak{N}$ we define $h_\alpha(x) = h^{\alpha-1} h_1(x)$ and obtain from 2.1 (3)

$$h_\alpha(x, t) = \begin{cases} 0 & \text{if} \quad 0 \leq t < x \\ (t - x)^{\alpha-1}/\Gamma(\alpha) & \text{if} \quad x < t < \infty \end{cases} \tag{1}$$

and $\mathrm{Re}\ \alpha > 0$. $h_1(x, t)$ is not a continuous function of x and t but $h_2(x, t)$ is, and $h_\alpha(x) = h^{\alpha-2} h_2(x)$ shows that for each $\alpha \in \mathfrak{N}$, $h_\alpha(x) \in C$ for all $x \geq 0$.
Next,

$$h_1(x) h_1(y) = \left\{ \int_0^t h_1(x, t - u) h_1(y, u)\, du \right\}.$$

The integrand is equal to 1 if $u \geq y$ and $t - u \geq x$ and vanishes otherwise. It follows that the integral vanishes if $t < x + y$, and is equal to $t - x - y$ if $t > x + y$. Thus $h_1(x) h_1(y) = h_2(x + y)$. Multiplying by $h^{\alpha+\beta-2}$, we have

$$h_\alpha(x) h_\beta(y) = h_{\alpha+\beta}(x + y). \tag{2}$$

for $x \geq 0$, $y \geq 0$, $\alpha \in \mathfrak{N}$, $\beta \in \mathfrak{N}$. This equation suggests the extension of $h_\alpha(x)$ to $x < 0$ by setting $h_\alpha(x) = h^{2\alpha}[h_\alpha(-x)]^{-1}$, $x < 0$. It can be verified that the function thus extended is $\in C$ for all x, and (2) holds for all (real) x and y and all $\alpha, \beta \in \mathfrak{N}$.

EXAMPLE 4. The function $h_0(x) = sh_1(x)$ is of particular importance in operational calculus. $h_0(0) = 1$, $h_0(x) h_0(y) = h_0(x + y)$, and, in particular, $[h_0(x)]^{-1} = h_0(-x)$, from example 3. Moreover, for $f \in C$ and $x > 0$,

$$h_0(x) \{f(t)\} = s \left\{ \int_0^t h_1(x, t - u) f(u)\, du \right\} = s \begin{cases} 0 & \text{if} \quad 0 \leq t \leq x \\ \int_0^{t-x} f(u)\, du & \text{if} \quad x \leq t < \infty \end{cases}$$

so that

$$h_0(x) \{f(t)\} = \begin{cases} 0 & \text{if} \quad 0 \leq t < x \\ f(t - x) & \text{if} \quad x < t < \infty \end{cases} \tag{3}$$

and $h_0(x)$, with $x > 0$, is the *shift operator*.

PROBLEMS

1. Show that

$$\{x^2 + t^2\} = x^2 h + 2h^3, \qquad \{x^2 + t^2\}^{-1} = \frac{s^3}{x^2 s^2 + 2}.$$

Give intervals I on which these operator functions are continuous.

2. $\phi(x)$ is a, possibly discontinuous, numerical function defined and locally integrable for all x. Show that

$$\left\{ \int_{x-t}^{x+t} \phi(y)\, dy \right\} \epsilon\ C\mathfrak{C} \qquad \text{and} \qquad \{\phi(x+t) + \phi(x-t)\} \epsilon\ C\mathfrak{F}$$

for all x.

3. $\phi(x)$ being a bounded continuous function for all x, what can you say about the continuity of the operator function

$$\left\{ \int_{-\infty}^{\infty} e^{-u^2} \phi(x + 2u \sqrt{t}\,)\, du \right\}.$$

4. Are $h_x(1)$, $h_x(-1)$ continuous operator functions?

5. Show that $h_\alpha(x) \to 0$ as $x \to \infty$.

6. Prove that

$$[1 - h_0(x)]^{-1} = \sum_{n=0}^{\infty} h_0(nx)$$

when $x > 0$.

7. Suppose that $\operatorname{Re} \alpha_n > \alpha$ for $n = 1, 2, \cdots$ and $x_n \to \infty$. Prove that the infinite series $\Sigma\, \gamma_n h_{\alpha_n}(x_n)$ is convergent for any choice of the coefficients $\gamma_n \epsilon\ \mathfrak{N}$. What can you say about the convergence of the infinite series $\Sigma\, c_n h_{\alpha_n}(x_n)$ when (i) $c_n \epsilon\ \mathfrak{C}$, (ii) $c_n \epsilon\ \mathfrak{F}$.

8. If $a \epsilon\ \mathfrak{F}$ and $ah_\alpha(-x)$ is a continuous function of x and t for all $x \geq 0$ and $t \geq 0$, show that $a = 0$.

3. If $a, b \epsilon\ \mathfrak{F}$ and $ah_\alpha(x) + bh_\alpha(-x)$ is a continuous function of x and t for all x and $t \geq 0$, show that $a = b = 0$.

4.4 Differentiation of Operator Functions

From now on $a'(x)$, $a''(x)$, $\cdots$, $a^{(n)}(x)$ will denote derivatives of the operator function $a(x)$ with respect to x. C^n will be the class of n times continuously differentiable operator functions, C^∞ the class of infinitely differentiable functions. C^0, $a^{(0)}(x)$, $\partial^0 a(x, t)/\partial x^0$ will be interpreted as C, $a(x)$, $a(x, t)$ respectively.

DEFINITION 13. $a(x) \epsilon\ C^n(I)$ if corresponding to each finite closed subinterval J of I there is a $p = p_J \neq 0$ so that $pa(x)$ is a function of x and t in D_J which has n continuous partial derivatives with respect to x in D_J. We set

$$a^{(n)}(x) = p^{-1} \left\{ \frac{\partial^n pa(x, t)}{\partial x^n} \right\}$$

in D_J.

The reader should verify that $a^{(n)}(x)$ is independent of p and that this process defines $a^{(n)}(x)$ uniquely in all of I. This notion of differentiation with respect to x has all the properties one would expect of it. Some of these are summarized in the following theorem.

THEOREM 12. (i) If $a(x) \in C^1(I)$ and $x_0 \in I$ then

$$\frac{a(x) - a(x_0)}{x - x_0} \to a'(x_0) \qquad \text{as} \qquad x \to x_0.$$

(ii) $a(x) = a \in \mathfrak{F}$ for all $x \in I$ if and only if $a(x) \in C^1(I)$ and $a'(x) = 0$ for $x \in I$.
(iii) If $a(x) \in C^n$ and $k < n$, then $a^{(k)}(x) \in C^{n-k}$. (iv) If $\phi(x) \in C^n\mathfrak{N}$, $a(x)$ and $b(x) \in C^n\mathfrak{F}$, then $a(x) + b(x)$, $\phi(x) a(x)$, $a(x) b(x) \in C^n\mathfrak{F}$ and derivatives of sums and products are computed according to the rules of elementary calculus.
(v) If $a(x)$ and $[a(x)]^{-1} \in C^1$, then

$$\left([a(x)]^{-1}\right)' = - [a(x)]^{-2} a'(x).$$

Proof. (i) For fixed t,

$$\lim_{x \to x_0} \frac{pa(x, t) - pa(x_0, t)}{x - x_0} = \frac{\partial pa(x_0, t)}{\partial x}.$$

Moreover, since $\partial pa(x, t)/\partial x$ is continuous in D_J, convergence is uniform for $x \in J$, $0 \leq t \leq T$, T being any fixed positive number. (ii) The derivative of a constant function is clearly zero. Conversely, suppose $a(x) \in C^1$, $a'(x) = 0$. For any J, there is a p so that $\partial pa(x, t)/\partial x = 0$ in D_J. It follows that $pa(x, t) = pa(t)$ is independent of x in J. Thus, $a(x)$ is independent of x in J and since J is any closed subinterval of I, $a(x)$ is constant in I. (iii) is obvious, and the easy verification of (iv) is left as an exercise. (v) Differentiate $a(x) [a(x)]^{-1} = 1$ to obtain $a'(x) [a(x)]^{-1} + a(x) \left([a(x)]^{-1}\right)' = 0$ according to (ii) and (iv). Note that it is necessary to assume that $[a(x)]^{-1} \in C^1$: this does not follow from $a(x) \in C^1$, $a(x) \neq 0$.

EXAMPLE 1. $\{\cos (x - t)\} \in C^\infty$ for all x, and

$$\{\cos (x - t)\}' = \{- \sin (x - t)\} = \frac{- s \sin x + \cos x}{s^2 + 1}$$

Note that this is in accordance with the result obtained by differentiating with respect to x the representation obtained in section 4.3, example 1.

EXAMPLE 2. To prove that for each $\alpha \in \mathfrak{N}$, $h_\alpha(x) \in C^\infty$ for all x, and $h'_\alpha(x) = - sh_\alpha(x)$. First assume Re $\alpha > 2$ and $x \geq 0$. Then it is seen from 4.3(1) that $h_\alpha(x)$ is continuously differentiable, and $h'_\alpha(x) = - h_{\alpha-1}(x) = - sh_\alpha(x)$. This result can be extended to all α and all x by means of 4.3(2). This result, together with $h_\alpha(0) = h^\alpha$ suggests the notation $h_\alpha(x) = h^\alpha e^{-xs}$ which will be justified in section 5.2.

PROBLEMS

1. Show that $\{x + t\}^{-1}$ and $\{x^2 + t^2\}^{-1}$ are differentiable operator functions, and find the derivatives of these functions.

2. If $\phi(x)$ and $\theta(x)$ are continuously differentiable numerical functions, and $a, b \in \mathfrak{F}$, show (without using theorem 12) that $\phi(x)\, a + \theta(x)\, b$ is continuously differentiable.

3. $\phi(x)$ is a numerical function that is continuous for all x. Show that the operator function

$$f(x) = \{\phi(x + t) + \phi(x - t)\} \in C^2 \qquad \text{and} \qquad f''(x) = s^2 f(x) - 2s\phi(x).$$

Does this result hold for sectionally continuous functions?
Under what conditions on $\phi(x)$ is $g(x) = \{\int_{x-t}^{x+t} \phi(y)\, dy\} \in C^2$? Prove that under appropriate conditions $g''(x) = s^2 g(x) - 2\phi(x)$.

4. $\phi(x)$ is a numerical function that is continuous for $x \geq 0$. Show that

$$(x) = \{\phi(x + t) + \operatorname{sgn}(x - t)\phi\,(|x - t|)\} \in C^2 \quad \text{and} \quad f''(x) = s^2 f(x) - 2s\phi(x)$$

for $x \geq 0$, and prove a corresponding result for

$$g(x) = \left\{\int_{|x-t|}^{x+t} \phi(y)\, dy\right\}.$$

4.5 Integration of Operator Functions

We first define integrals over a finite closed interval $I = [\alpha, \beta]$ and then we define infinite integrals as limits.

DEFINITION 14. For $\phi(x)$ an absolutely integrable numerical function, $a(x) \in C\mathfrak{F}(I)$, $p = p_I$ so that $pa(x) \in C\mathfrak{C}(I)$,

$$\int_\alpha^\beta a(x)\, \phi(x)\, dx = p^{-1} \left\{ \int_\alpha^\beta pa(x, t)\, \phi(x)\, dx \right\}.$$

The reader should verify that the integral is independent of p and has all the usual properties, in particular, those summarized in theorem 13 where it is assumed that all the integrals exist.

THEOREM 13.

(i) $\displaystyle\int_\alpha^\alpha = 0, \qquad \int_\alpha^\beta = -\int_\beta^\alpha, \qquad \int_\alpha^\gamma + \int_\gamma^\beta = \int_\alpha^\beta$

(ii) $\displaystyle\int_\alpha^\beta \sum_{i=1}^m a_i(x) \sum_{j=1}^n \phi_j(x)\, dx = \sum_{i=1}^m \sum_{j=1}^n \int_\alpha^\beta a_i(x)\, \phi_j(x)\, dx$

(iii) $\displaystyle\int_\alpha^\beta c\,\phi(x)\,dx = c\int_\alpha^\beta \phi(x)\,dx,$ $\displaystyle\int_x^\beta c\,a(x)\,\phi(x)\,dx = c\int_\alpha^\beta a(x)\,\phi(x)\,dx$

(iv) $\displaystyle\int_\alpha^\beta a'(x)\,dx = a(\beta) - a(\alpha)$ if $a(x) \in C^1(I).$

[The formula for integration by parts follows from this result and theorem 12 (iv).]

(v) If $a(x) \in C(I)$, then

$$b(x) = \int_\alpha^x a(y)\,dy \in C^1(I) \qquad \text{and} \qquad b'(x) = a(x).$$

(vi) Change of the variable of integration is effected as in numerical integrals.

DEFINITION 15. If $\int_\alpha^\beta$ exists, for a fixed α and all $\beta > \alpha$, in the sense of definition 14, and $\lim \int_\alpha^\beta$, as $\beta \to \infty$, exists in the sense of definition 12(i), then we say that the infinite integral $\int_\alpha^\infty$ exists, or is convergent, and set $\int_\alpha^\infty = \lim \int_\alpha^\beta$ as $\beta \to \infty$. There is a corresponding definition of $\int_{-\infty}^\alpha$, and $\int_{-\infty}^\infty$ is said to exist if $\int_\alpha^\infty$ and $\int_{-\infty}^\alpha$ exist for some α.

THEOREM 14 $\int_0^\infty h_0(v)f(v)\,dv$ exists and is equal to f for every $f \in \mathfrak{R}$.

Proof $f(v)$ is a numerical function which is absolutely integrable over $0 \le x \le T$ for any $T > 0$. Moreover, $h^2 h_0(x) = h_0(x)$ is a continuous function of x and t for $x \ge 0$, $t \ge 0$, and hence

$$h^2 \int_0^T h_0(x)\,f(x)\,dx = \left\{\int_0^T h_2(x,\,t)\,f(x)\,dx\right\}$$

for any $T > 0$. By 4.3(1), the right-hand side is

$$\left\{ \begin{array}{ll} \int_0^t (t-x)\,f(x)\,dx & 0 \le t \le T \\[2mm] \int_0^T (t-x)\,f(x)\,dx & T \le t < \infty \end{array} \right\} = h^2 \left\{ \begin{array}{ll} f(t) & 0 \le t < T \\ 0 & T \le t < \infty \end{array} \right\} = h^2 f_T(t),$$

say. Since $f_T \to f$ uniformly (in the sense of definition 7), as $T \to \infty$, the proof of theorem 14 is complete.

If the notation suggested at the end of the preceding section is used, our result appears in the striking form

$$\int_0^\infty e^{-xs}\,f(x)\,dx = f \qquad\qquad f \in \mathfrak{R} \qquad (1)$$

which provides the background for the connection between functions of s and Laplace transforms.

PROBLEMS

1. For $f \in \Re$ and $0 \le x_1 < x_2$ show that

$$\int_{x_1}^{x_2} h_0(x) f(x) \, dx = \begin{cases} f(t) & \text{if} & x_1 < t < x_2 \\ 0 & & \text{otherwise} \end{cases}.$$

2. For $f \in \Re$ and any $\alpha \in \Re$ prove that $\int_0^\infty h_\alpha(x) f(x) \, dx$ exists and is equal to $h^\alpha f$.

3. Let $a, b, \in \mathfrak{F}; f(x) \in C(I); x, x_1, x_2 \in I$. Show that

$$z(x) = ah_0(x) + bh_0(-x) + \tfrac{1}{2} \int_{x_1}^{x} h_1(x - y) f(y) \, dy$$

$$- \tfrac{1}{2} \int_{x_2}^{x} h_1(y - x) f(y) \, dy$$

$\in C^2(I)$ and satisfies the differential equation $z''(x) - s^2 z(x) = f(x)$.

4. Let $\phi(x)$ be a numerical function which is twice continuously differentiable for all x. Take $f(x) = \phi(x)$, $x_1 = -\infty$, $x_2 = \infty$ in problem 3 and find conditions on a and b that will ensure that $z(x) = \{z(x, t)\}$ is a twice continuously differentiable function of x and t for $t \ge 0$ and all x. Show also that in this case $z(x, t)$ satisfies the partial differential equation

$$\frac{\partial^2 z}{\partial x^2} - \frac{\partial^2 z}{\partial t^2} = 0.$$

[5]

Differential Equations for Operator Functions. Exponential Functions

5.1 The Equation $z'(x) - wz(x) = 0$

The simplest differential equation involving an unknown operator function, $z(x)$, is

$$z'(x) - wz(x) = 0 \qquad (1)$$

where w is a fixed convolution quotient. A *solution* of (1) on the interval I is an operator function $z(x) \in C^1(I)$ which satisfies (1).

The differential equation (1) always possesses the *trivial solution* $z(x) = 0$ for all x: it may or may not possess other solutions. It is seen from section 4.4, example 2, that (1) possesses a nontrivial solution if $w = s$. On the other hand, it can be proved [Mikusiński (1959) p. 410 f.] that the trivial solution is the only solution of (1) if $w = s^2$.

THEOREM 15. If (1) possesses a nontrivial solution on some interval then (i) (1) possesses infinitely differentiable nontrivial solutions for all x; (ii) corresponding to each (real) x_0 and each $z_0 \in \mathfrak{F}$, $z_0 \neq 0$, there is exactly one such solution, $z(x)$, satisfying $z(x_0) = z_0$; (iii) such solutions vanish nowhere; and (iv) they satisfy $z(x) z(y) = z(0) z(x + y)$ for all real x, y.

Proof. (i) We shall prove that a nontrivial solution $z(x)$ given on a closed interval $x_1 \leq x \leq x_2$ can be extended indefinitely. Now, if such a solution vanishes for $x_1 < x < x_2$, then it also vanishes by continuity at x_1 and x_2. This being impossible, there is an x_0 between x_1 and x_2 for which $z(x_0) - z_0 \neq 0$. We shall use the relation (iv) informally to define an extension. We set

$$x_3 = 2x_2 - x_0 > x_2 \qquad \text{and} \qquad z_1(x) = z_0^{-1} z(x_2) z(x - x_2 + x_0)$$

for $x_2 \leq x \leq x_3$. Since under these circumstances $x_1 < x - x_2 + x_0 \leq x_2$, we have $z_1(x) \in C^1$, and $z_1'(x) = wz(x)$ by a simple computation. Moreover, $z_1(x_2) = z(x_2)$, $z_1'(x_2) = z'(x_2)$, so that the function $Z(x)$ defined by

$$Z(x) = \begin{matrix} z(x) & \text{if} & x_1 \leq x \leq x_2 \\ z_1(x) & \text{if} & x_2 \leq x \leq x_3 \end{matrix}$$

is continuously differentiable, and satisfies (1), for $x_1 \leq x \leq x_3$. Proceeding in this manner, the interval $x_1 \leq x \leq x_2$ can be extended in both directions.

Every extension to the right has at least the length of $x_2 - x_0$, and every extension to the left, $x_0 - x_1$. Thus every finite interval can be reached in a finite number of steps. The function $z(x)$ so constructed is at least in C^1 for all x. Suppose $z(x) \epsilon C^k$. Then $z'(x) = wz(x) \epsilon C^k$ so that $z(x) \epsilon C^{k+1}$. It follows that $z(x) \epsilon C^{\infty}$.

(iii) Suppose $z(x_0) = 0$, let y be an arbitrary fixed real number, and consider $Z(x) = z(x) z(2y - x)$. Now, $Z(x) \epsilon C^1$ for all x,

$$Z'(x) = z'(x) z(2y - x) - z(x) z'(2y - x)$$

$$= wz(x) z(2y - x) - z(x) wz'(2y - x) = 0,$$

and $Z(x)$ is constant by theorem 12 (ii). It follows that $Z(x) = Z(x_0) = 0$, and in particular, $Z(y) = [z(y)]^2 = 0$ so that $z(y) = 0$. Since y was arbitrary, $z(y)$ vanishes identically.

(ii) Suppose $z(x)$ is any nontrivial solution. Then $z_1(x) = z_0[z(x_0)]^{-1} z(x)$ is clearly a nontrivial solution, and $z_1(x_0) = z_0$. If $z_1(x)$ and $z_2(x)$ are two such solutions satisfying $z_1(x_0) = z_2(x_0) = z_0$, then $z_1(x) - z_2(x)$ is a solution that vanishes at x_0, and hence identically.

(iv) Let $z(x)$ be any solution of (1) for all x, and let y be an arbitrary fixed real number. Then $Z(x) = z(x) z(y) - z(0) z(x + y)$ is easily seen to be a solution of (1) for all x, $Z(0) = 0$, and hence $z(x)$ vanishes identically.

PROBLEMS

1. If $z(x)$ is any nontrivial solution of (1), show that $[z(x)]^{-1}$ is infinitely differentiable.

2. Assuming that (1) possesses nontrivial solutions, let $z(x)$ be that solution of (1) satisfying $z(0) = 1$. Prove that for $f(x) \epsilon C$ for all x, the differential equation

$$Z'(x) - wZ(x) = f(x)$$

has exactly one solution satisfying $Z(x_0) = z_0$, and that this solution is given by

$$Z(x) = z_0 z(x - x_0) + \int_{x_0}^{x} z(x - y) f(y) \, dy.$$

5.2 Logarithms and Exponential Functions

DEFINITION 16. (i) $w \epsilon \mathfrak{F}$ is called a *logarithm* if 5.1(1) possesses a nontrivial solution. (ii) A solution of 5.1(1) satisfying $z(0) = 1$ is denoted by e^{xw} or $\exp{(xw)}$ and called an *exponential function*.

The basic properties of exponential functions follow from theorem 15.

THEOREM 16. An exponential function, if it exists, is unique, infinitely differentiable for all x, and vanishes nowhere. Moreover, $e^{xw} e^{yw} = e^{(x+y)w}$ and in particular $(e^{xw})^{-1} = e^{-xw}$.

At present no general criteria are known for logarithms. The only general result known is

THEOREM 17. Logarithms form a vector space over the field of real numbers; that is, if α, β are real numbers and u, v are logarithms, then $\alpha u + \beta v$ is a logarithm.

Proof. $z(x) = e^{\alpha x u} e^{\beta x v} \in C^\infty$ for all x, $z(0) = 1$, and

$$z'(x) = \alpha u e^{\alpha x u} e^{\beta x v} + e^{\alpha x u} \beta v e^{\beta x v} = (\alpha u + \beta v) z(x).$$

Hence $e^{\alpha x u} e^{\beta x v} = e^{(\alpha u + \beta v)x}$.

EXAMPLE 1. Every locally integrable function is a logarithm, and

$$e^{xf} = \sum_{n=0}^{\infty} \frac{x^n}{n!} f^n \qquad\qquad f \in \Re.$$

The infinite series converges by theorem 10(i) (see also section 4.2, problem 4). Moreover, the estimate 4.1(4) with $\alpha = 0$ shows that the series $\Sigma_{n=0}^\infty x^n h f^n(t)/n!$ converges uniformly if x and t are restricted to finite intervals. The series represents a function, $g(x, t)$, that is continuous for $t > 0$ and all x. By uniform convergence of the differentiated series, $\partial g(x, t)/\partial x$ exists, is a continuous function of x and t for $t > 0$ and all x, and may be computed by term-by-term differentiation, thus,

$$\frac{\partial g(x, t)}{\partial x} = \sum_{n=1}^{\infty} \frac{x^{n-1}}{(n-1)!} h f^n(t).$$

It follows that $g(x) \in C^1$ for all x, $g'(x) = fg(x)$, and $g(0) = h$ so that $g(x) = h e^{xf}$.

EXAMPLE 2. The delta function is a logarithm and $e^{x \cdot 1} = e^x \cdot 1$ where e^x is the numerical exponential function. $i \cdot 1$ is also a logarithm, and the corresponding exponential function is $e^{ix} \cdot 1$.

Other examples of exponential functions occur in the next section. Here we merely mention that s^α is a logarithm if and only if $\alpha \leq 1$ and is^α, if and only if $\alpha < 1$ [Mikusiński (1959) p. 399 f]. The case $\alpha = 1$ shows clearly that the restriction in theorem 17 to real multipliers is necessary.

PROBLEMS

1. For Re $\nu > -1$ and arbitrary complex α show that

$$h^{\nu+1} e^{-\alpha h} = \left\{ \left(\frac{t}{\alpha} \right)^{\nu/2} J_\nu(2 \sqrt{\alpha t}) \right\}.$$

2. For $0 < \alpha < 1$, $\gamma > 0$, $x > 0$ show that

$$\exp(-s^\alpha x) = \left\{ \frac{1}{2\pi i} \int_{\gamma - i\infty}^{\gamma + i\infty} \exp(zt - z^\alpha x)\, dz \right\},$$

where the principal branch of z^α is taken in the integrand. Show also that x may be complex in this formula provided that $|\arg x| < (1 - \alpha)\,\pi/2$.

5.3 exp $(-xs)$ and exp $(-x\sqrt{s})$

It follows from section 4.4, example 2, that s is a logarithm and $e^{xs} = h_0(-x)$. From section 4.3, example 4, e^{-xs} for $x > 0$ is the shift operator. It may be mentioned that the exponential series $\Sigma\,(xs)^n/n!$ is not convergent but $(1 + xs/n)^n \to e^{xs}$ as $n \to \infty$ [Mikusiński and Ryll-Nardzewski (1951)].

e^{-xs}, for $x > 0$, is not a locally integrable function but it transforms locally integrable functions into such functions (section 4.3, example 4.) It follows that e^{xs} cannot be a locally integrable function for then $e^{-xs}\, e^{xs} = 1$ would have to be such a function. In connection with the application of exponential functions to partial differential equations it is of interest to know under what circumstances $ae^{xs} + be^{-xs}$ with $a, b \in \mathfrak{F}$ represent, say, continuous functions of x and t. The answer is contained in theorem 18.

DEFINITION 16. $\mathfrak{C}_0$ is the class of continuous functions of t vanishing at $t = 0$.

THEOREM 18. Let $a \in \mathfrak{F}$, $b \in \mathfrak{F}$. Then (i) $ae^{xs} \in C\mathfrak{C}$ for $x \geq x_0$ if and only if $a = 0$; (ii) $be^{-xs} \in C^k\mathfrak{C}$ for $x \geq x_0$ if and only if $s^k b e^{-x_0 s} \in \mathfrak{C}_0$; (iii) $ae^{xs} + be^{-xs} \in C^k\mathfrak{C}$ for $x \geq x_0$ if and only if $a = 0$ and $s^k b e^{-x_0 s} \in \mathfrak{C}_0$; and (iv) $ae^{xs} + be^{-xs} \in C^k\mathfrak{C}$ for $x \leq x_0$ if and only if $s^k a e^{x_0 s} \in \mathfrak{C}_0$ and $b = 0$.

COROLLARY. $ae^{xs} + be^{-xs} \in C\mathfrak{C}$ for all x if and only if $a = b = 0$.

Proof. (i) By assumption, $c_0 = ae^{x_0 s}$ and $c = ae^{xs}$ for an arbitrary fixed $x > x_0$ are both $\in \mathfrak{C}$. Moreover, $c_0 = ce^{-(x - x_0)s}$, and by equation 4.3(3), $c_0(t) = 0$ for $0 \leq t < x - x_0$. Since x is arbitrary, and c_0 is independent of x, $c_0 = 0$ and hence $a = e^{-x_0 s} c_0 = 0$. (ii) $c = be^{-x_0 s} \in \mathfrak{C}$, and

$$be^{-xs} = e^{-(x - x_0)s}\, c = \begin{cases} 0 & 0 \leq t < x - x_0 \\ c(t - x + x_0) & x - x_0 < t < \infty \end{cases}$$

will be k times continuously differentiable with respect to x for $x \geq x_0$ if and only if $c(t)$ is k times continuously differentiable with respect to t, and $c(0) = c'(0) = \cdots = c^{(k)}(t) = 0$. But then $s^k c = s^k b e^{-x_0 s} = \{c^{(k)}(t)\}$ by theorem 7, and $s^k c \in \mathfrak{C}_0$. (iii) There exists a $q \in \mathfrak{C}$ so that $q \neq 0$ and $q\, b\, e^{-x_0 s} \in \mathfrak{C}$. Then $h^{k+1}\, qb e^{-x_0 s}$ is a k times continuously differentiable function of t which vanishes at $t = 0$ together with its first k derivatives. It follows that $h^{k+1}\, qb e^{-xs} \in C^k\mathfrak{C}$, and consequently also $h^{k+1}\, qa e^{xs} \in C^k\mathfrak{C}$, for $x \geq x_0$. Then $a = 0$ by (i), and

(ii) applies. (iv) follows from (iii) (replace x and x_0 by $-x$ and $-x_0$), and the corollary follows from (iii) and (iv).

We now turn to $\exp(x\sqrt{s})$ and first introduce the functions $Q(x, t)$ and $R(x, t)$. $Q(x, 0) = R(x, 0) = 0$, and

$$Q(x, t) = \frac{x}{2\sqrt{\pi t^3}} \exp - \frac{x^2}{4t} \qquad t > 0 \tag{1}$$

$$R(x, t) = \frac{1}{\sqrt{\pi t}} \exp - \frac{x^2}{4t} \qquad t > 0.$$

We also introduce the operator functions $Q(x) = \{Q(x, t)\}$ and $R(x) = \{R(x, t)\}$.

$Q(x, t)$ is continuous and, in fact, infinitely differentiable for all x and $t \geq 0$, except at $x = t = 0$. For fixed x, $Q(x, t) \to 0$ as $t \to 0$ or $t \to \infty$; and for fixed $t \geq 0$, $Q(x, t) \to 0$ as $x \to 0$ or $x \to \pm\infty$. Note, however, that $Q(x, t)$ is unbounded if $x \to 0$, $t \to 0$ in such a manner that x^2/t is a nonzero constant. $R(x, t)$ has similar properties, except that $R(0, t) = (\pi t)^{-1/2}$. Lastly,

$$Q(x, t) = -\frac{\partial R(x, t)}{\partial x}. \tag{2}$$

For fixed $x > 0$,

$$\frac{\partial \log Q(x, t)}{\partial t} = -\frac{3}{2t} + \frac{x^2}{4t^2}$$

so that $Q(x, t)$, considered as a function of t, increases when t increases from 0 to $x^2/6$ and decreases as t continues to increase. Hence

$$0 \leq Q(x, t) \leq Q\left(x, \frac{x^2}{6}\right) = \frac{3}{x^2}\sqrt{\frac{6}{\pi e^3}} \qquad x > 0, \tag{3}$$

THEOREM 19. $\sqrt{s}$ is a logarithm and $\exp(-x\sqrt{s}) = Q(x)$ when $x > 0$.

Proof. We shall first prove $Q'(x) = -\sqrt{s}\, Q(x)$ when $x > 0$. Actually, it is easier to prove the equivalent result $[hQ(x)]' = -\sqrt{h}\, Q(x)$. Now,

$$hQ(x) = \left\{ \frac{x}{2\sqrt{\pi}} \int_0^t \exp\left(-\frac{x^2}{4u}\right) \frac{du}{u^{3/2}} \right\} = \left\{ \frac{2}{\sqrt{\pi}} \int_{x/(2\sqrt{t})}^\infty e^{-v^2}\, dv \right\} \tag{4}$$

is continuously differentiable with respect to x when $x > 0$, and $[hQ(x)]' = -R(x)$. Also

$$\sqrt{h}\, Q(x) = \left\{ \frac{x}{2\sqrt{\pi}\, \Gamma(\frac{1}{2})} \int_0^t (t - u)^{-1/2}\, u^{-3/2} \exp\left(-\frac{x^2}{4u}\right) du \right\}$$

and if we introduce a new variable of integration v by the substitution

$$\frac{x^2}{4u} = \frac{x^2}{4t} + v^2$$

we obtain

$$\sqrt{h}\, Q(x) = \left\{ \frac{2}{\sqrt{\pi t}\ \Gamma(\tfrac{1}{2})} \int_0^\infty \exp\left(-v^2 - \frac{x^2}{4t}\right) dv \right\} = R(x). \qquad x \geq 0. \qquad (5)$$

By comparison with (4), $Q'(x) + \sqrt{s}\, Q(x) = 0$. Thus we have a nontrivial solution of the differential equation; it remains to show that $Q(x) \to 1$ as $x \to 0$.

We see from (4) that for each $t > 0$, $\int_0^t Q(x, u)\, du \to 1$ as $x \to 0 +$. The convergence, however, is not uniform. On the other hand from (5) we have

$$h^{3/2} Q(x) = \left\{ \int_0^t R(x, u)\, du \right\} = \left\{ \int_0^t \exp\left(-\frac{x^2}{4u}\right) \frac{du}{\sqrt{\pi u}} \right\}.$$

As $x \to 0$, the right-hand side approaches, uniformly in $0 \leq t \leq T$ for each $T > 0$,

$$\left\{ \int_0^t \frac{du}{\sqrt{\pi u}} \right\} = h^{3/2},$$

thus showing that $Q(x) \to 1$ and completing the proof.

It should be noted that the validity of the relation $\exp(-x\sqrt{s}) = Q(x)$ is restricted to $x > 0$. $Q(0) = 0$ while $\exp(-0 \cdot \sqrt{s}) = 1$, and for $x > 0$, $\exp(x\sqrt{s})$ is not a locally integrable function since otherwise $\exp(-x\sqrt{s})$ $\times \exp(x\sqrt{s}) = 1$ would have to be locally integrable.

In the application of these exponential functions to parabolic partial differential equations it is convenient to know something about the functional character of $\exp(\pm x\sqrt{s})$. The results one obtains correspond to theorem 18 on e^{xs} but they are somewhat different in character.

DEFINITION 17. (i) A numerical function, $\phi(x)$, defined for $x \geq x_0$ is said to be of *slow growth* as $x \to \infty$ if for every $\epsilon > 0$, $\phi(x) \exp(-\epsilon x^2) \to 0$ as $x \to \infty$. (ii) An operator function, $f(x) = \{f(x, t)\}$, defined for $x \geq x_0$ is said to be of slow growth if $f(x) \in \mathfrak{R}$ for each $x \geq x_0$ and $\int_0^t |f(x, u)|\, du$ is a numerical function of slow growth for each $t > 0$. (iii) There are similar definitions for $x \to -\infty$ and $x \to \pm\infty$.

A numerical function, $\phi(x)$, is clearly of slow growth if and only if the operator function, $\phi(x) f$, is of slow growth for each $f \in \mathfrak{R}$; and it can be proved that the sum and convolution (in the numerical case, product) of functions of slow growth is again of slow growth.

THEOREM 20. (i) If $f(x)$ is an operator function of slow growth, then $f(x) \exp(-x\sqrt{s}) \to 0$ uniformly as $x \to \infty$. (ii) If $a \exp(x\sqrt{s})$ is of slow growth as $x \to \infty$, then $a = 0$. (iii) If $a \exp(x\sqrt{s}) + b \exp(-x\sqrt{s})$ is of slow growth as $x \to \pm\infty$, then $a = b = 0$.

Proof. (i) Fix $T > 0$, let $0 \le t \le T$, and consider only sufficiently large values of x for which $x^2 > 6T$. By the remarks preceding theorem 19, $Q(x, t)$ is an increasing function of t, and in fact $0 \le Q(x, t) \le Q(x, T)$. Set

$$g(x) = f(x) \exp(-x\sqrt{s}) = \{g(x, t)\} .$$

Then

$$|g(x, t)| = \left| \int_0^t Q(x, t-u) f(x, u) \, du \right| \le Q(x, T) \int_0^T |f(x, u)| \, du$$

or

$$|g(x, t)| \le \frac{x}{4\sqrt{\pi T^3}} \exp\left(-\frac{x^2}{4T}\right) \int_0^T |f(x, u)| \, du.$$

The right-hand side tends to zero, and hence $g(x, t) \to 0$ uniformly for $0 \le t \le T$ as $x \to \infty$. (ii) $f(x) = a \exp(x\sqrt{s})$ is of slow growth and $a = f(x) \exp(-x\sqrt{s})$. The right-hand side approaches zero as $x \to \infty$ by (i). Since a is independent of x, $a = 0$. (iii) First let $x > 0$. $b = p/q$ where $p, q \in \mathfrak{C}$. Then $qb \exp(-x\sqrt{s}) \in C\mathfrak{C}$ and since a function of slow growth is locally integrable for each x, $q a \exp(x\sqrt{s}) \in \mathfrak{R}$ for each $x > 0$. Moreover, $qb \exp(x\sqrt{s})$ is of slow growth as $x \to \infty$ and hence $qa \exp(x\sqrt{s})$ is of slow growth. It follows from (ii) that $a = 0$. $b = 0$ can be proved similarly upon making $x \to -\infty$.

As a matter of fact, assertions (ii) and (iii) can be proved under less restrictive conditions on the operator functions, $f(x)$, in question, assuming merely that for each $t > 0$ there exist a $\delta = \delta(t)$ so that $\exp(-\delta x^2) \int_0^t |f(x, u| \, du \to 0$ as $x \to \infty$; but this extension of theorem 20 will not be proved here.

PROBLEMS

1. For $0 \le x < y$ show that

$$s^{-1}(e^{-rs} - e^{-vs}) - \begin{cases} 1 & \text{if} \quad x \le t \le y \\ 0 & \text{otherwise} \end{cases} .$$

Show also that $s^{-3}(e^{-xs} - e^{-ys})$ is a function, and determine this function. Is it continuous? Continuously differentiable?

2. Prove that

$$(1 - e^{-xs})^{-1} = \sum_{n=0}^{\infty} e^{-nxs}$$

when $x > 0$ and deduce that

$$s^{-1}(1 - e^{-xs})^{-1} = \left\{ \left[\frac{t}{x} \right] \right\},$$

where $[y]$ is the largest integer $\le y$.

For $f \in \Re$ show that

$$\frac{f}{1 - e^{-xs}} = \left\{ \sum_{0 \le n \le t/x} f(t - nx) \right\} \qquad x > 0$$

and more generally that

$$\frac{f}{(e^{xs} + y)^\alpha} = \left\{ \sum_{0 \le n \le t/x - \alpha} \binom{-\alpha}{n} y^n f(t - nx - \alpha x) \right\} \qquad x > 0,\ \alpha > 0.$$

3. $f \in \Re$ and $f(t) = 0$ when $t \ge T \ge 0$; $g(t) = f(t)$ when $0 \le t < T$ and $g(t + T) = g(t)$ for all $t \ge 0$. Show that $g = f/(1 - e^{-Ts})$.

4. Show that

$$\frac{1}{s^2 + x^2} \frac{1 + e^{-\pi s/x}}{1 - e^{-\pi s/x}} = \left\{ \frac{|\sin xt|}{x} \right\} \qquad x > 0.$$

5. Use section 4.2, example 2, to prove that r is a logarithm, and show that

$$e^{-x(r-s)} = 1 - \left\{ \frac{x\gamma}{\sqrt{t^2 + 2xt}} J_1(\gamma \sqrt{t^2 + 2xt}) \right\} \qquad x \ge 0.$$

$$r^{-1} e^{-x(r-s)} = \left\{ J_0(\gamma \sqrt{t^2 + 2xt}) \right\} \qquad x \ge 0.$$

6. Prove that

$$\frac{\sinh xs}{\cosh ys} = \sum_{n=0}^{\infty} (-1)^n e^{(x - (2n+1)y)s} - \sum_{n=0}^{\infty} (-1)^n e^{-(x + (2n+1)y)s}$$

for $y > 0$ and all real x. Here

$$\sinh xs = \frac{e^{xs} - e^{-xs}}{2}, \qquad \cosh xs = \frac{e^{xs} + e^{-xs}}{2}.$$

7. For which values of the real parameters x and y is $\sinh xs/(s \cosh ys)$ a function?
Verify that for $0 \le x \le y$

$$\frac{\sinh xs}{s \cosh ys} = \left\{ \frac{2}{\pi} \sum_{n=1}^{\infty} \frac{(-1)^{n-1}}{n - \frac{1}{2}} \sin (n - \tfrac{1}{2}) \frac{\pi x}{y} \sin (n - \tfrac{1}{2}) \frac{\pi t}{y} \right\}.$$

8. Show that

$$\frac{1}{s} e^{-x\sqrt{s}} = \left\{ \text{Erfc} \frac{x}{2\sqrt{t}} \right\} \qquad x > 0$$

where

$$\text{Erfc } z = \frac{2}{\sqrt{\pi}} \int_z^{\infty} e^{-v^2} \, dv.$$

Show also that

$$\sqrt{s}\, e^{-x\sqrt{s}} = \left\{\frac{x^2 - 2t}{4\sqrt{\pi t^5}}\right\} \exp\left\{-\frac{x^2}{4t}\right\}, \qquad x > 0$$

and express $s^{-3/2} \exp\left(-x\sqrt{s}\right)$ in terms of the error function.

9. Prove that $\exp\left(-x\sqrt{s + \alpha}\right) = \left\{e^{-\alpha t} Q(x, t)\right\}$ for $x > 0$.

10. Define $Q(z)$ for complex values of z. Let α be a fixed complex number, $-\pi/4 < \arg \alpha < \pi/4$. Prove that $\alpha\sqrt{s}$ is a logarithm, and $\exp\left(-x\alpha\sqrt{s}\right) = Q(\alpha x)$ when $x > 0$.
Is $i\sqrt{s}$ a logarithm?

11. $\phi(x)$ is a numerical function for which $x^{-2}\log|\phi(x)| \to 0$ as $x \to \infty$. Prove that $\phi(x)$ is of slow growth.

12. Prove that the sum and convolution of two functions of slow growth is again of slow growth.

13. If $a(x)\exp\left(x\sqrt{s}\right)$ is of slow growth as $x \to \infty$, show that $a(x) \in \mathfrak{R}$ for each sufficiently large x, and $a(x) \to 0$ uniformly as $x \to \infty$.

14. Use problem 5 to investigate e^{-xr}. Does this exponential function have properties analogous to the properties of e^{-xs} described in theorem 18?

5.4 The Differential Equation $z''(x) - w^2z(x) = f(x)$

Throughout this section we assume that w is a logarithm so that the exponential functions e^{xw} and e^{-xw} exist and theorem 16 holds.

First let us consider the homogeneous equation

$$z''(x) - w^2z(x) = 0. \tag{1}$$

For any $a, b \in \mathfrak{F}$,

$$ae^{xw} + be^{-xw} \tag{2}$$

is clearly a solution of (1); and we wish to show that every solution is of this form.

LEMMA 6. Let $z(x)$ be a solution of (1) on the interval I. If $z(x_0) = z'(x_0) = 0$ for some $x_0 \in I$ then $z(x)$ vanishes identically on I.

Proof. Let J be the largest subinterval of I containing x_0 and such that $z(x)$ vanishes identically on J. An endpoint of J that is in the interior of I must belong to J by continuity of $z(x)$. We wish to show that such an endpoint cannot exist. Suppose, then, that the left endpoint, x_1, of J is an interior point of I. For

$$Z(x) = [z'(x)]^2 - [wz(x)]^2$$

we have

$$Z'(x) = 2z'(x)\, z''(x) - 2w^2 z(x) z'(x) = 0$$

so that $Z(x)$ is constant on I. Since $Z(x)$ vanishes on J, it must vanish identically on I so that

$$[z'(x) - wz(x)]\,[z'(x) + wz(x)] = 0$$

on I. Moreover, each of the two factors here being a continuous function of x, at least one of the factors must vanish identically in some interval $x_3 < x \le x_1$. Since $z(x_1) = 0$, it follows from theorem 15(iii) that $z(x)$ vanishes identically for $x_3 < x \le x_1$ but this is impossible since J was the largest interval of its kind. Similarly, the right endpoint of J cannot be an interior point of I so that $J = I$, and the lemma is established.

THEOREM 21. Given I, $x_0 \in I$, and z_0, $z_0' \in \mathfrak{F}$, (1) has exactly one solution on I satisfying $z(x_0) = z_0$, $z'(x_0) = z_0'$, and this solution is of the form (2).

   Proof.

$$z_1(x) = \tfrac{1}{2}(z_0 + w^{-1}z_0')\,e^{xw} + \tfrac{1}{2}(z_0 - w^{-1}z_0')\,e^{-xw} \tag{3}$$

is of the form (2) and clearly satisfies (1) and the given conditions. Suppose there is a second such solution, $z_2(x)$. Then $z(x) = z_1(x) - z_2(x)$ is a solution, $z(x_0) = z'(x_0) = 0$, and $z(x)$ vanishes identically in I by lemma 6.

   Incidentally we have also proved that every solution of (1) can be extended to the entire real axis.

We now turn to the inhomogeneous equation

$$z''(x) - w^2 z(x) = f(x) \tag{4}$$

a particular solution of which may be obtained by variation of parameters in the form

$$z_0(x) = -\frac{1}{2w}\left[\int_{x_1}^{x} e^{(y-x)w} f(y)\, dy + \int_{x}^{x_2} e^{(x-y)w} f(y)\, dy\right], \tag{5}$$

where x_1 and x_2 are any two points of I. We shall not give the derivation of (5): it is sufficient to note that $z_0(x)$ can be shown, by explicit computation of $z_0''(x)$, to satisfy (4).

THEOREM 22. For $f(x) \in C(I)$, any solution of (4) can be written in the form

$$z(x) = ae^{xw} + be^{-xw} + z_0(x), \tag{6}$$

where a, $b \in \mathfrak{F}$, $z_0(x)$ is given by (5), and x_1, $x_2 \in I$.

   Proof. Let $z(x)$ be a solution (4). If $f(x) \in C(I)$, then $z_0(x)$ is also a solution of (4) on I and hence $z(x) - z_0(x)$, a solution of (1) and of the form (2) by lemma 6. This proof also shows that x_1 and x_2 may be chosen arbitrarily in I, whereupon a and b are determined.

If I is a finite interval, there are usually two boundary conditions for the determination of a and b in (2) or (6). In the case of a semi-infinite or infinite interval, properties of the exponential function such as the properties of e^{xs} and $e^{x\sqrt{s}}$ stated in theorems 18 and 20 are used to determine a and b. In the applications to partial differential equations this leads to uniqueness theorems.

PROBLEMS

1. Determine that solution of (4) which vanishes at x_1 and x_2.

2. Let $\phi(x)$ be a numerical function that is continuous for all x. Show that the general solution of the differential equation

$$z''(x) - s^2z(x) = \phi(x)s \tag{7}$$

can be written in the form

$$z(x) = ae^{xs} + be^{-xs} - \tfrac{1}{2}\{\phi(x+t) + \phi(x-t)\}.$$

Show also that $-\tfrac{1}{2}\{\phi(x+t) + \phi(x-t)\}$ is the only solution of (7) that is $\epsilon\ C\mathfrak{C}$ for all x, and find the most general solution of (7) that is $\epsilon\ C\mathfrak{C}$ for $x \geq 0$. [Hint: Set $x_1 = -\infty$, $x_2 = \infty$ in (5) and use section 4.4, problem 3 and theorem 18.]

3. $\phi(x)$ is a numerical function that is locally integrable and is of slow growth as $x \to \pm\infty$. Show that the general solution of the differential equation

$$z''(x) - sz(x) = \phi(x) \tag{8}$$

can be written in the form

$$z(x) = ae^{x\sqrt{s}} + be^{-x\sqrt{s}} - \frac{1}{\sqrt{\pi}} \left\{ \int_{-\infty}^{\infty} e^{-u^2} \phi(x + 2u\sqrt{t})\, du \right\}.$$

Show that (8) has a unique solution which is of slow growth as $x \to \pm\infty$ and determine this solution. Determine also the most general solution of (8) that is of slow growth as $x \to \infty$.

4. Investigate the differential equation

$$z''(x) - r^2z(x) = \phi(x)$$

where $r^2 = s^2 + \gamma^2$ and $\phi(x)$ is a numerical function that is continuous for all x. Obtain results for this equation which are analogous to the results, in problem 2, for (7). [Hint: Use 5.3 problems 5 and 14.]

5. Show that solutions of the differential equation

$$z''(x) + \frac{1}{x} z'(x) - s^2z(x) = 0 \qquad\qquad x > 0$$

are of the form $a\,I_0(xs) + bK_0(xs)$, where $a, b \in \mathfrak{F}$ and

$$I_0(xs) = e^{xs} \begin{cases} \pi^{-1}(2xt - t^2)^{-1/2} & 0 < t < 2x \\ 0 & 2x < t < \infty \end{cases}$$

$$K_0(xs) = \begin{cases} 0 & 0 \leq t < x \\ (t^2 - x^2)^{-1/2} & x < t < \infty \end{cases}.$$

5.5 Difference Equations

The shift operator, e^{-xs}, may be used for the solution of linear difference equations with constant coefficients, recurrence relations, difference-differential equations, and similar functional equations involving values of the unknown function with a "timelag." In the case of recurrence relations, the unknown is a sequence of numbers, $z_0, z_1, z_2, \cdots$, rather than a function. There are two methods for converting such a recurrence relation into a functional equation which can be handled by operational calculus. One of these is based on the use of an unknown function $z = \{z(t)\}$, commonly a step function, for which $z(k) = z_k$ for $k = 0, 1, 2, \cdots$, and the other, on the use of the operator

$$Z = \sum_{k=0}^{\infty} z_k e^{-ks}.$$

Since

$$hZ(k) = z_0 + z_1 + \cdots + z_k$$

and hence $(1 - e^{-s})hZ$ is a step function whose value at $t = k$ is z_k, the two methods are closely related; and the second method is also closely related to the classical technique of generating functions.

Several examples will be given to illustrate the application of operational calculus to such problems. In these, $\omega > 0$, α and β are (given) real or complex numbers, f, g are given functions which are defined, and locally integrable, on $t \geq 0$; and the unknown function, z, is also assumed to be locally integrable on $t \geq 0$.

EXAMPLE 1. Our first example is a simple *difference equation of the first order*,

$$z(t) - z(t - \omega) = f(t) \qquad\qquad t \geq 0. \qquad (1)$$

In order to have a well-defined problem, we must prescribe the values of $z(t - \omega)$ when $t - \omega < 0$. We do this by adjoining to (1) the *initial condition*

$$z(t - \omega) = g(t) \qquad\qquad 0 \leq t < \omega. \qquad (2)$$

[Alternatively, we could prescribe the values of $z(t)$ for $0 \leq t < \omega$ and restrict (1) to $t \geq \omega$.] $g(t)$ is given, and is absolutely integrable, for $0 \leq t < \omega$. We complete the definition of this function by setting $g(t) = 0$ for $t \geq \omega$.

Now

$$z(t - \omega) - g(t) = \begin{array}{ll} 0 & \text{when} \quad 0 \leq t < \omega \\ z(t - \omega) & \text{when} \quad t \geq \omega \end{array},$$

so that $\{z(t - \omega\} - g = e^{-\omega s}z$, and thus the equation

$$z - e^{-\omega s}z = f + g \tag{3}$$

in convolution quotients contains both the difference equation (1) and the initial condition (2). [A similar situation arises with regard to differential equations, *cf.* equation 3.3(5).]

The solution of (3) is $z = (1 - e^{-\omega s})^{-1}(f + g)$. By section 5.3 problem 2,

$$(1 - e^{-\omega s})^{-1}f = \sum_{n=0}^{[t/\omega]} f(t - n\omega),$$

where $[t/\omega]$ is the largest integer $\leq t/\omega$; and the corresponding formula for g simplifies to

$$(1 - e^{-\omega s})^{-1}g = g\left(t - \left[\frac{t}{\omega}\right]\omega\right)$$

since $g(t) = 0$ when $t \geq \omega$. Thus, the solution of (1), (2) is

$$z(t) = g\left(t - \left[\frac{t}{\omega}\right]\omega\right) + \sum_{n=0}^{[t/\omega]} f(t - n\omega) \qquad t \geq 0. \tag{4}$$

Actually, (1) and (2) on the one hand and (3) on the other hand are not equivalent; indeed, (3) means only that (1) and (2) are satisfied almost everywhere (*cf.* the remarks following definition 5). Correspondingly, not only (4) but also any function that is equivalent (in the sense of definition 5) to (4) satisfies (3). The solution (4) is distinguished by two properties: (i) it satisfies (1), (2) for every (rather than almost every) t, and (ii) if (1), (2) possess a continuous solution, that solution will be given by (4). It should be noted, though, that (1), (2) may not possess a continuous solution even if f and g are continuous. Indeed,

$$z(k\omega) = g(0) + \sum_{n=0}^{k} f[(k - n)\omega],$$

and this is also the limit to which $z(t)$ tends as t approaches $k\omega$ from the right. On the other hand, if t approaches $k\omega$ from the left, $[t/\omega] = k - 1$ during the approach, and the limit will accordingly be

$$g(\omega) + \sum_{n=0}^{k-1} f[(k - n)\omega],$$

and it turns out that for continuous f and g, (3) possesses a continuous solution solution (which is then unique) if and only if $f(0) = g(\omega) - g(0)$.

Because of property (i), (4) is regarded as *the* solution of (1), (2).

EXAMPLE 2. Next we turn to a *recurrence relation of the first order* with constant coefficients,

$$z_k + \alpha z_{k-1} = f_k \qquad\qquad k = 0, 1, 2, \cdots$$

with the initial condition $z_{-1} = g_0$. [If z_0 is prescribed, take $g_0 = (f_0 - z_0)/\alpha$.]

We turn this problem into one resembling that of example 1 by regarding z_k as the value at $t = k$ of an unknown locally integrable function $z = \{z(t)\}$, and using two functions f and g that are locally integrable and such that $f(k) = f_k$ for $k = 0, 1, 2, \cdots$, $g(0) = g_0$, and $g(t) = 0$ for $t \geq \omega$. For instance, we may take $f(t) = f_k$ for $k \leq t < k + 1$, $g(t) = g_0$ for $0 \leq t < 1$, $g(t) = 0$ for $t \geq 1$, but any other definition will do equally well.

We now have

$$z(t) + \alpha z(t - 1) = f(t) \qquad t \geq 0, \qquad\qquad z(t - 1) = g(t) \qquad 0 \leq t < 1,$$

or $z + \alpha e^{-s} z = f - \alpha g$ in the operational form. The solution may be obtained as in example 1 and upon setting $t = k$ we have the solution of the recurrence relation in the form

$$z_k = (-\alpha)^{k+1} g_0 + \sum_{n=0}^{k} (-\alpha)^n f_{k-n}.$$

EXAMPLE 3. Our next example is a simple *difference-differential equation* of the first order

$$z'(t) - z(t - \omega) = f(t) \qquad\qquad t \geq 0$$

with the initial condition

$$z(t - \omega) = g(t) \qquad\qquad 0 \leq t \leq \omega.$$

Here z must be assumed to be differentiable, and hence continuous, so that the ambiguity present in example 1 will disappear. Furthermore, we assume that $z(t)$ is the integral of its derivative so that equation 3.1(4) holds. Lastly, in this case $z(0)$ must also be prescribed, and accordingly $g(t)$ vanishes only for $t > \omega$ (rather than $t \geq \omega$).

Under these assumptions,

$$\{z'(t)\} = sz - z(0) = sz - g(\omega), \qquad \{z(t - \omega)\} = e^{-\omega s} z + g,$$

and instead of (3) we obtain in this case

$$sz - e^{-\omega s} z = f + g + g(\omega),$$

which we may write as

$$(1 - he^{-\omega s})z = [f + g + g(\omega)]h.$$

$he^{-\omega s} \epsilon \, \Re$, and this function vanishes identically for $0 \leq t < \omega$. By section 4.2, example 1, $(1 - he^{-\omega s})^{-1}$ possesses a convergent expansion in powers of $he^{-\omega s}$, and we have

$$z = \sum_{n=0}^{\infty} e^{-n\omega s} h^{n+1} [f + g + g(\omega)].$$

The evaluation of $z(t)$ is left as an exercise for the reader.

EXAMPLE 4. We conclude with a *recurrence relation of the second order*

$$z_k - (\alpha + \beta)z_{k-1} + \alpha\beta z_{k-2} = f_k \qquad k = 0, 1, 2, \cdots$$

and the corresponding *difference equation of the second order*

$$z(t) - (\alpha + \beta) z(t - 1) + \alpha\beta z(t - 2) = f(t) \qquad t \geq 0$$

with the initial conditions $z_{-1} = g(1)$, $z_{-2} = g(0)$ and $z(t - 2) = g(t)$ for $0 \leq t < 2$, respectively. $g(t) = 0$ for $t \geq 2$ and we write $g(t + 1) = g_1(t)$. As in example 1, $\{z(t - 1)\} = e^{-s}z + g_1$, $\{z(t - 2)\} = e^{-2s}z + g$, and hence the operational form,

$$[1 - (\alpha + \beta)e^{-s} + \alpha\beta e^{-2s}]z - f + (\alpha + \beta)g_1 - \alpha\beta g$$

of the difference equation. By decomposition in partial fractions and subsequent expansion

$$[1 - (\alpha + \beta)e^{-s} + \alpha\beta e^{-2s}]^{-1} = \sum_{n=0}^{\infty} \frac{\alpha^{n+1} - \beta^{n+1}}{\alpha - \beta} e^{-ns},$$

and the application of this expansion yields the solution of the difference equation in the form

$$z(t) = \frac{\alpha^{[t]+2} - \beta^{[t]+2}}{\alpha - \beta} g(t - [t] + 1) - \alpha\beta \frac{\alpha^{[t]+1} - \beta^{[t]+1}}{\alpha - \beta} g(t - [t])$$

$$+ \sum_{n=0}^{[t]} \frac{\alpha^{n+1} - \beta^{n+1}}{\alpha - \beta} f(t - n)$$

and, with $t = k$, the solution of the recurrence relation in the form

$$z_k = \frac{\alpha^{k+2} - \beta^{k+2}}{\alpha - \beta} z_{-1} - \alpha\beta \frac{\alpha^{k+1} - \beta^{k+1}}{\alpha - \beta} z_{-2} + \sum_{n=0}^{k} \frac{\alpha^{n+1} - \beta^{n+1}}{\alpha - \beta} f_{k-n}.$$

Difference-differential equations of higher orders, integro-differential equations of the convolution type, and systems of functional equations with time lag may be handled by similar techniques.

PROBLEMS

Solve the following functional equations with the assigned initial conditions.

1. $z(t) - z(t - \omega) = e^t$ for $t \geq 0$; $z(t) = 0$ for $-\omega \leq t < 0$.

2. $z(t) - 2z(t - \omega) + z(t - 2\omega) = f(t)$ for $t \geq 0$; $z(t) = 0$ for $-2\omega \leq t < 0$.

3. $z_k - 5z_{k-1} + 6z_{k-2} = 0$ for $k = 0, 1, 2, \cdots$; $z_{-2} = 0$, $z_{-1} = 1$.

4. $z''(t) + \alpha^2 z(t - 2\omega) = f(t)$ for $t \geq 0$; $z(t - 2\omega) = g(t)$ for $0 \leq t \leq 2$.

5. $z_1(t) - z_2(t - 1) = f(t)$, $z_2(t) - z_1(t - 1) = g(t)$ for $t \geq 0$, $z_1(t) = z_2(t) = 0$ for $-1 \leq t < 0$.

[6]

The One-dimensional Wave Equation

6.1 Operational Form of the Wave Equation

In this and in the following chapter we shall denote partial derivatives by subscripts. Thus,

$$z_x(x, t) = \frac{\partial z(x, t)}{\partial x}, \qquad z_t(x, t) = \frac{\partial z(x, t)}{\partial t}, \qquad z_{xx}(x, t) = \frac{\partial^2 z(x, t)}{\partial x^2}$$

and so on, $z_x(x) = \{z_x(x, t)\}$ and so on.

The *one-dimensional wave equation* is the partial differential equation

$$z_{xx}(x, t) = z_{tt}(x, t) \tag{1}$$

in which the velocity of wave propagation has been taken to be unity. We shall investigate this differential equation when x ranges over an interval I while $t \geq 0$. A *solution* of (1) is a function $z(x, t)$ that is twice continuously differentiable and satisfies (1) in D: $x \in I$, $t \geq 0$. For such a function,

$$z(x) = \{z(x, t)\} \in C^2\mathfrak{C},$$

and

$$z_{tt}(x) = s^2 z(x) - z_t(x, 0) - s z(x, 0) \tag{2}$$

holds by theorem 7.

If *initial conditions*

$$z(x, 0) = \phi(x), \qquad z_t(x, 0) = \psi(x) \tag{3}$$

are prescribed, (1) and (2) lead to the *operational form* of the wave equation,

$$z_{xx}(x) - s^2 z(x) = - s\phi(x) - \psi(x). \tag{4}$$

The initial conditions are incorporated in the operational form while boundary conditions, if there are any, must be adjoined to it.

Some typical problems involving (1) are as follows.

Infinite range. Here I is the infinite interval $-\infty < x < \infty$, and there are no boundary conditions.

Semi-infinite range. Here I is a semi-infinite interval $x_0 \leq x < \infty$, say, and a single boundary condition is prescribed at $x = x_0$. Frequently either $z(x_0)$ or $z_x(x_0)$ is given but other boundary conditions occur.

75

Finite range. Here I is a finite closed interval, and there are two boundary conditions, usually one at each end. The boundary conditions are of the same nature as in the case of a semi-infinite interval.

In order to solve (1), we seek solutions of (4), in the first instance in $C^2\mathfrak{C}$. In general, elements of $C^2\mathfrak{C}$ are not necessarily differentiable with respect to t, but in the case of solutions of (4) we have

$$z(x) = h\phi(x) + h^2\psi(x) + h^2 z_{xx}(x)$$

and here each term on the right-hand side is a twice continuously differentiable function of t so that at any rate z_t and z_{tt} exist and are continuous in D. It is not obvious that z_{xt} also exists but upon explicit representation of the solution this turns out to be the case.

Operational methods are particularly suitable for the discussion of *generalized solutions* of the wave equation. These are solutions of (4) in $C^2\mathfrak{F}$ rather than $C^2\mathfrak{C}$. Such solutions do not necessarily possess partial derivatives in the ordinary sense but $z_{xx}(x)$ will exist in the sense of definition 13 and $z_{tt}(x)$, in the sense of (2). In general $z_{xx}(x)$ and $z_{tt}(x)$ will be generalized functions (operator functions) and the wave equation will be satisfied in the sense of equality between generalized functions.

A somewhat more general partial differential equation, sometimes called the *telegraphist's equation,* is

$$z_{xx}(x, t) = z_{tt}(x, t) + 2\kappa z_t(x, t) + \gamma z(x, t).$$

It leads to the differential equation

$$z_{xx}(x) = (s^2 + 2\kappa s + \gamma) z(x) - z_t(x, 0) - (s + 2\kappa) z(x, 0)$$

for the operator function $z(x) = \{z(x, t)\}$. If we set $w(x, t) = e^{\kappa t} z(x, t)$ we obtain

$$w_{xx}(x, t) = w_{tt}(x, t) + (\gamma - \kappa^2) w(x, t),$$

so that we may assume $\kappa = 0$ without any loss of generality.

Other partial differential equations may be treated by similar methods. The equation of spherically symmetric waves in n dimensions is

$$z_{xx}(x, t) + \frac{n-1}{x} z_x(x, t) = z_{tt}(x, t)$$

where x is the distance from the centre of the waves. Here the operator function $z(x) = \{z(x, t)\}$ satisfies the differential equation

$$z_{xx}(x) + \frac{n-1}{x} z_x(x) = s^2 z(x) - sz(x, 0) - z_t(x, 0).$$

There are many other, more or less similar problems.

PROBLEMS

1. The linearized theory of sound waves in an exponential loudspeaker horn leads to the partial differential equation

$$z_{xx}(x, t) + \alpha\, z_x(x, t) = c^{-2}\, z_{tt}(x, t),$$

where x is the coordinate measured along the axis of the horn, t is time, c is the velocity of sound in free air, α is the flaring index (the cross section at abscissa x being $A\, e^{\alpha x}$), and $z(x, t)$ is the velocity potential. Obtain the corresponding differential equation for the operator function $z(x) = \{z(x, t)\}$; and discuss this equation.

2. $z(x, t)$ is continuously differentiable for $t \geq 0$ and all x, and $z(x, t)$ satisfies the partial differential equation $z_x(x, t) + x\, z_t(x, t) = 0$ together with the boundary conditions $z(x, 0) = 0$, $z(0, t) = t^2$. Obtain the differential equation satisfied by the operator function $s(x) = \{s(x, t)\}$ and hence or otherwise find $z(x, t)$.

6.2 The Infinite Interval

The operational form of the wave equation, equation 6.1(4), is a special case of equation 5.4(4). Accordingly, we take $w = s$, $f(x) = -s\phi(x) - \psi(x)$ in 5.4(5) and choose $x_1 = -\infty$, $x_2 = \infty$, obtaining

$$s(x) = \tfrac{1}{2} \int_{-\infty}^{x} e^{-(x-u)s}[\phi(y) + h\psi(y)]\, dy + \tfrac{1}{2} \int_{x}^{\infty} e^{-(u-x)s}[\phi(y) + h\psi(y)]\, dy.$$

By a change in the variable of integration this becomes

$$z(x) = \tfrac{1}{2} \int_{0}^{\infty} e^{-us}[\phi(x + u) + \phi(x - u) + h\psi(x + u) + h\psi(x - u)]\, du$$

and by equation 4.5(1),

$$z(x) = \tfrac{1}{2}\{\phi(x + t) + \phi(x - t)\} + \tfrac{1}{2} h\{\psi(x + t) + \psi(x - t)\}.$$

Moreover,

$$h\{\psi(x + t) + \psi(x - t)\} = \left\{ \int_{0}^{t} \psi(x + u)\, du + \int_{0}^{t} \psi(x - u)\, du \right\}$$

$$= \left\{ \int_{x-t}^{x+t} \psi(y)\, dy \right\},$$

so that finally

$$z(x, t) = \tfrac{1}{2}\left[\phi(x + t) + \phi(x - t) + \int_{x-t}^{x+t} \psi(y)\, dy \right]. \tag{1}$$

THEOREM 23. Let $\phi(x)$ be continuously differentiable and $\psi(x)$ continuous for all x. Then (1) defines a generalized solution of the wave equation. This solution is continuously differentiable for $t \geq 0$ and all x, satisfies 6.1(3), and is unique in the class of continuous functions of x and t.

Proof. Under the assumptions of the theorem, (1) defines a continuously differentiable function of x, t,

$$z_t(x, t) = \tfrac{1}{2}[\phi'(x + t) - \phi'(x - t) + \psi(x + t) + \psi(x - t)],$$

and equation 6.1(3) is clearly satisfied. By section 4.4, problem 3,

$$z_{xx}(x) = s^2 z(x) - s\phi(x) - \psi(x),$$

and since $z_{tt}(x)$ is defined by 6.1(2), $z_{xx}(x) = z_{tt}(x)$.

To prove uniqueness in $C\mathfrak{C}$ we remark that the difference, $Z(x)$, of two generalized solutions of the wave equation satisfying the same initial conditions is a solution of the differential equation $Z_{xx}(x) - s^2 Z(x) = 0$ and hence is of the form $ae^{xs} + be^{-xs}$. Since $Z(x) \epsilon C\mathfrak{C}$ for all x, it follows from the corollary of theorem 18 that $a = b = 0$.

The conditions imposed upon ϕ in theorem 23 may be relaxed somewhat, in particular the assumption of continuity of ϕ' may be replaced by the assumption that

$$\int_a^b \phi'(y)\, dy = \phi(b) - \phi(a)$$

for all real a and b, that is, by the assumption that ϕ possesses a locally integrable derivative. The condition of differentiability of ϕ may be dropped altogether provided that the existence of z_t as a function of x and t is not demanded and the initial conditions are interpreted as being implicit in equation 6.1(4). On the other hand, a discussion of section 4.4, problem 3, shows that the continuity of ϕ and ψ is a necessary condition as long as differentiation with respect to x is interpreted in the sense of section 4.4.

PROBLEMS

1. Show that (1) represents a twice continuously differentiable solution of the initial value problem if and only if ϕ is twice continuously differentiable and ψ is continuously differentiable.

2. Describe wave motion in an infinite medium when $z(x, 0) = 0$ for $x < 0$ and $= x$ for $x \geq 0$, and $z_t(x, 0) = 0$ for all x. Show that in this case the generalized derivatives can be expressed in terms of the delta function; and verify that $z_{xx} = z_{tt}$ is a valid equation in generalized functions.

3. Solve the partial differential equation $z_x(x, t) + x z_t(x, t) = 0$ for $t \geq 0$ and all x when $z(x, 0) = 0$ and $z(0, t) = t$. Is the solution you obtain a generalized solution?

6.3 The Semi-infinite Interval

We now turn to the wave equation in the semi-infinite interval $x \geq 0$ prescribing, in addition to the initial conditions of equation 6.1(3), the *boundary condition*

$$z(0, t) = c(t). \tag{1}$$

We again use equation 5.4(5) with $w = s$, $f(x) = -s\phi(x) - \psi(x)$ and choose $x_1 = 0$, $x_2 = \infty$ in equation 5.4(5) and $a = 0$ in equation 5.4(6), the choice of a being suggested by theorem 18(i). Thus we obtain

$$z(x) = be^{-xs} + \tfrac{1}{2} \int_0^x e^{-(x-y)s}[\phi(y) + h\psi(y)]\, dy$$

$$+ \tfrac{1}{2} \int_x^\infty e^{-(y-x)s}[\phi(y) + h\psi(y)]\, dy.$$

From (1),

$$c = z(0) = b + \tfrac{1}{2} \int_0^\infty e^{-ys}[\phi(y) + h\psi(y)]\, dy$$

and substituting b from here in equation (2) and changing the variable of integration,

$$z(x) = ce^{-xs} - \tfrac{1}{2} e^{-xs} \int_0^\infty e^{-ys}[\phi(y) + h\psi(y)]\, dy$$

$$+ \tfrac{1}{2} \int_0^x e^{-ys}[\phi(x - y) + h\psi(x - y)]\, dy$$

$$+ \tfrac{1}{2} \int_0^\infty e^{-ys}[\phi(x + y) + h\psi(x + y)]\, dy.$$

Each term on the right-hand side is a function of x and t. In the first and third integral we use theorem 14 and in the second, section 4.5, problem 1, to obtain

$$ce^{-xs} - \tfrac{1}{2} e^{-xs} \int_0^\infty e^{-ys}[\phi(y) + h\psi(y)]\, dy$$

$$= \begin{cases} 0 & 0 < t < x \\ c(t - x) - \tfrac{1}{2}\phi(t - x) - \tfrac{1}{2}\int_0^{t-x} \psi(y)\, dy & x < t < \infty \end{cases}$$

$$\tfrac{1}{2} \int_0^x e^{-ys}[\phi(x - y) + h\psi(x - y)]\, dy$$

$$= \tfrac{1}{2} \begin{cases} \phi(x - t) + \int_{x-t}^x \psi(y)\, dy & 0 < t < x \\ \int_0^x \psi(y)\, dy & x < t < \infty \end{cases}$$

$$\tfrac{1}{2} \int_0^\infty e^{-ys}[\phi(x + y) + h\psi(x + y)]\, dy = \tfrac{1}{2}\left\{ \phi(x + t) + \int_x^{x+t} \psi(y)\, dy \right\}.$$

Adding the last three evaluations,

$$z(x, t) = \tfrac{1}{2}\left[\phi(x + t) + \phi(x - t) + \int_{x-t}^{x+t} \psi(y)\,dy\right] \qquad 0 < t < x \tag{3}$$

$$z(x, t) = c(t - x) + \tfrac{1}{2}\left[\phi(x + t) - \phi(t - x) + \int_{t-x}^{t+x} \psi(y)\,dy\right] \qquad x < t < \infty$$

or, more concisely,

$$z(x) = ce^{-xs} + \tfrac{1}{2}\left\{\phi(x + t) + \text{sgn}\,(x - t)\,\phi(|x - t|) + \int_{|x-t|}^{x+t} \psi(y)\,dy\right\}. \tag{4}$$

THEOREM 24. Let $\phi(x)$ be continuously differentiable, and $\psi(x)$ continuous, for $x \geq 0$, and let $c \,\epsilon\, \mathfrak{C}$. Then (4) defines a generalized solution of equation 6.1(1). This solution is continuous, except possibly for $x = t$, is continuously differentiable when $t < x$, satisfies (1) and equation 6.1(3); and it is unique.

Proof. The statements about the continuity and differentiability of $z(x, t)$ are seen to be true upon inspection of (3), and the verification of (1) and equation 6.1(3) also follows. The verification of the wave equation is similar to that carried out in the preceding section except that section 4.4, problem 4, must be used in place of problem 3.

Uniqueness will be proved in $C\mathfrak{F}$. Suppose $Z(x)$ is the difference of two solutions of 6.1(4) satisfying (1) and 6.1(3). Then

$$Z_{xx}(x) - s^2Z(x) = 0 \qquad \text{and} \qquad Z(0) = 0.$$

It follows that $Z(x) = a(e^{xs} - e^{-xs})$, and since there exists a nonzero $p \,\epsilon\, \mathfrak{C}$ for which $pZ(x)$ is a continuous function of x and t for $x \geq 0$, $t \geq 0$, $a = 0$ by theorem 18(iii).

As in the case of the infinite interval, the conditions of theorem 24 may be relaxed somewhat.

It may be mentioned that the change of sign of $\text{sgn}\,(x - t)\,\phi(|x - t|)$ at $t = x$ expresses the effect of reflection at the end $x = 0$ and that the term ce^{-xs} expresses the propagation of the "signal" fed into the system at $x = 0$.

PROBLEMS

1. Show that the necessary and sufficient conditions for the existence of a twice continuously differentiable solution of equations 6.1(1), (3) and 6.3(1) are that $\phi(x)$ be twice continuously differentiable, and $\psi(x)$ continuously differentiable, for $x \geq 0$, $c(t)$ twice continuously differentiable for $t \geq 0$, $c(0) = \phi(0)$, $c'(0) = \psi'(0)$, and $c''(0) = \phi''(0)$.

2. Using section 6.1, problem 1, obtain a description of the sound waves in a semi-infinite horn, $x \geq 0$, given that the air is initially at rest, and given

also the air velocity, $-z_t(0, t) = v(t)$ at the throat. [Reference: McLachlan, 1953, p. 288 f.]

3. A solution of the wave equation in the semi-infinite range $x \geq 0$ is determined by the initial conditions $z(x, 0) = \phi(x)$, $z_t(x, 0) = \psi(x)$ and the boundary condition $z_x(0, t) = v(t)$. Obtain this solution, and describe conditions on the data that will make $z(x, t)$ (i) a twice continuously differentiable solution, (ii) a generalized solution.

6.4 The Finite Interval

Here we take I to be the closed interval $x_1 \leq x \leq x_2$ and prescribe, in addition to the initial conditions of equation 6.1(3), the boundary conditions

$$z(x_1, t) = c_1(t), \qquad z(x_2, t) = c_2(t). \tag{1}$$

Since the general formulas are somewhat involved, we shall content ourselves with a brief indication of the method for obtaining the solution in the general case, and then will discuss two special cases. Actually, the solution in the general case is a sum of solutions such as the ones discussed in examples 1 and 2 below.

We again use equations 5.4(5), 5.4(6) with $w = s$, $f(x) = -s\phi(x) - \psi(x)$, and undetermined a and b. The boundary conditions (1) provide two linear algebraic equations for a and b of the form

$$ae^{x_1 s} + be^{-x_1 s} = p_1$$

$$ae^{x_2 s} + be^{-x_2 s} = p_2$$

where p_1 and p_2 are certain generalized functions involving c_1, c_2, ϕ, ψ. The determinant of this system is

$$e^{(x_1 - x_2)s} - e^{(x_2 - x_1)s} = -e^{(x_2 - x_1)s}[1 - e^{-2(x_2 - x_1)s}]$$

and is different from zero by theorem 16 and section 5.3, problem 2. It follows that a and b are uniquely determined, the solution may be written down explicitly and analyzed.

THEOREM 25. Let $\phi(x)$ be continuously differentiable and $\psi(x)$ continuous for $x_1 \leq x \leq x_2$, and let c_1, $c_2 \in \mathfrak{C}$. Then the process described above yields a generalized solution of equation 6.1(1). This solution is continuous except possibly along the lines $x - t = x_1 - k(x_2 - x_1)$, $x + t = x_2 + k(x_2 - x_1)$, $k = 0, 1, 2, \cdots$, and it is differentiable when $t < x - x_1$ and $t < x_2 - x$. It satisfies equation 6.1(3) for $x_1 < x < x_2$ and (1) for $t \neq k(x_2 - x_1)$, $k = 0, 1, 2, \cdots$; and it is unique.

EXAMPLE 1. To solve 6.1(1) for $0 \leq x \leq L$, $t \geq 0$, subject to the conditions

$$z(x, 0) = z_t(x, 0) = z(0, t) = 0, \qquad z(L, t) = c(t).$$

This problem may be interpreted as that of the motion of a string of length L, initially at rest, with one endpoint fixed while the other end undergoes a prescribed motion (receives an "input signal") $c(t)$.

The solution of equation 6.1(4) in this case is $z(x) = ae^{xs} + be^{-xs}$, and the boundary conditions give

$$a + b = 0, \qquad ae^{Ls} + be^{-Ls} = c$$

so that the solution is

$$z(x) = \frac{e^{xs} - e^{-xs}}{e^{Ls} - e^{-Ls}} c. \tag{2}$$

By section 5.3, problem 2, we have

$$\frac{e^{xs} - e^{-xs}}{e^{Ls} - e^{-Ls}} = \frac{e^{-(L-x)s} - e^{-(L+x)s}}{1 - e^{-2Ls}} = [e^{-(L-x)s} - e^{-(L+x)s}] \sum_{k=0}^{\infty} e^{-2kLs}$$

$$= e^{-(L-x)s} - e^{-(L+x)s} + e^{-(3L-x)s} - e^{-(3L+x)s} + \cdots$$

and hence

$$z(x) = e^{-(L-x)s}c - e^{-(L+x)s}c + e^{-(3L-x)s}c - \cdots \tag{3}$$

Each term of this series is a continuous function except at one of the lines $t = (2k + 1)L \pm x$, $k = 0, 1, 2, \cdots$, and in each finite interval $0 \leq t \leq T$ only a finite number of the functions on the right-hand side of (3) is different from zero. The solution vanishes, and hence is certainly differentiable, when $t < L - x$, and the initial conditions are clearly satisfied, and so are the boundary conditions.

The expansion (3) admits of a simple interpretation. Each term vanishes when $0 \leq t < L - x$. At time $t = L - x$ the signal (which starts at $x = L$) reaches the point with coordinate x and is received there, delayed but undistorted: $z(x, t) = c(t - L + x)$ for $L - x < t < L + x$. At time $t = L + x$ the second term of the series ceases to be zero: it represents the signal that travelled along the string, was reflected at the fixed end $x = 0$ (the $-$ sign is due to a change of phase upon reflection), and now reaches the point with coordinate x. For $L + x < t < 3L - x$ we have

$$z(x, t) = c(t - L + x) - c(t - L - x),$$

a superposition of the direct and the once reflected signal. At time $t = 3L - x$ a twice reflected signal arrives. It has traversed the string twice, was reflected at each of the two ends: it is represented by the third term of (3). And so on.

EXAMPLE 2. To solve equation 6.1(1) for $0 \leq x \leq L$, $t \geq 0$, subject to the conditions

$$z(x, 0) = \phi(x), \qquad z_t(x, 0) = z(0, t) = z(L, t) = 0.$$

This is the problem of a string of length L with both endpoints fixed. The initial displacement is $\phi(x)$, the initial velocity is zero.

From 5.4(6),

$$z(x) = ae^{xs} + be^{-xs} + \tfrac{1}{2} \int_0^x e^{-(x-y)s} \phi(y) \, dy + \tfrac{1}{2} \int_x^L e^{-(y-x)s} \phi(y) \, dy.$$

The equations determining a and b are

$$0 - a + b + \tfrac{1}{2} \int_0^L e^{-ys} \phi(y) \, dy$$

$$0 = ae^{Ls} + be^{-Ls} + \tfrac{1}{2} \int_0^L e^{-(L-y)} \phi(y) \, dy.$$

Elimination of a and b leads to

$$z(x) = \int_0^L \frac{e^{(L-|x-y|)s} + e^{-(L-|x-y|)s} \cdot e^{(L-x-y)s} - e^{-(L-x-y)s}}{2(e^{Ls} - e^{-Ls})} \phi(y) \, dy,$$

Here $(e^{Ls} - e^{-Ls})^{-1}$ can be expanded in powers of e^{-2Ls} and after breaking up the integral in two parts, one from 0 to x and the other from x to L, section 4.5, problem 1, can be applied to each integral to give a series expansion of the solution.

PROBLEMS

1. Formulate conditions on c under which (3) represents a twice continuously differentiable solution of the wave equation.

2. If c is merely locally integrable (rather than continuous), does (2) represent a generalized solution of the wave equation?

3. Find explicit formulas for $z(x, t)$ of example 2 for $0 \leq t < L$. [Hint: You will have to expect different formulas according as $x - t$ and $L - x - t$ are positive or negative.]

4. Using the result of problem 3, formulate conditions under which the solution will be twice continuously differentiable.

5. Use operational calculus to solve the partial differential equation

$$c^2 z_{xx}(x, t) = z_{tt}(x, t) + g,$$

c and g being given positive constants, it being given that

$$z(x, 0) = z_t(x, 0) = z(0, t) = z(L, t) = 0.$$

Interpret the solution in terms of waves.

6. Obtain and discuss generalized solutions of the initial-boundary value problem: $z_{xx}(x, t) = z_{tt}(x, t)$ for $0 \le x \le L$, $t \ge 0$; $z(0, t) = z_x(L, t) = 0$, $z(x, 0) = 0$, $z_t(x, 0) = \psi(x)$.

[7]

The One-dimensional Diffusion Equation

7.1 Operational Form of the Diffusion Equation

As in the preceding chapter, we shall denote partial derivatives by subscripts.

The *one-dimensional diffusion equation* is the partial differential equation

$$z_{xx}(x, t) = z_t(x, t) \tag{1}$$

in which the diffusivity has been taken to be unity. We shall investigate this equation when (x, t) ranges over D as in Chapter 6. A *solution* of (1) is a function $z(x, t)$ that is twice continuously differentiable with respect to x, continuously differentiable with respect to t, and satisfies (1), in D. If an *initial condition*,

$$z(x, 0) = \phi(x) \tag{2}$$

is prescribed, the operator function $z(x) = \{z(x, t)\}$ corresponding to a solution is in $C^2\mathfrak{C}$ and satisfies the differential equation

$$z_{xx}(x) - sz(x) = -\phi(x) \tag{3}$$

which we call the *operational form* of the diffusion equation. The initial condition is incorporated in this operational form while boundary conditions, if there are any, must be adjoined to it. The boundary conditions are generally of the same nature as in the case of the wave equation except that in the case of infinite or semi-infinite intervals some growth restrictions are needed to make the solutions unique. The need for these growth restrictions, and indeed their nature, is suggested by theorem 20; and the different behavior of the wave equation and the diffusion equation in this respect is mirrored in the difference in character between theorems 18 and 20.

Solutions of (3) in $C^2\mathfrak{C}$ are indeed solutions of (1) and (2), for

$$z(x) = h\phi(x) + hz_{xx}(x)$$

or

$$z(x, t) = \phi(x) + \int_0^t z_{xx}(x, u) \, du$$

for such solutions.

85

As in the case of the wave equation, the introduction of *generalized solutions* seems desirable; and operational methods lend themselves to the introduction of such solutions. It should be noted, though, that the generalized solutions to be used here differ in their nature considerably from those used in the preceding chapter. In the case of the wave equation we relaxed differentiability conditions throughout D but retained the initial and boundary conditions. The resulting generalized solutions were continuous in D, with the possible exception of certain lines, and satisfied the initial and boundary conditions except where those lines meet the boundary of D; but the partial derivatives of the functions in question existed only in a generalized sense, and the wave equation was satisfied in the sense of equality of generalized functions. In the case of the diffusion equation it will turn out that our generalized solutions are infinitely differentiable in the *interior* of D (indeed they are analytic but we shall not prove this), and satisfy the diffusion equation there. They fail to be solutions (in the more restrictive sense) because they are not necessarily continuous at the boundary of D, and do not satisfy the initial and boundary conditions except in some generalized sense.

For instance, we shall obtain the solution of (1), (2) for the infinite interval $-\infty < x < \infty$ in the form

$$z(x, t) = \frac{1}{\sqrt{\pi}} \int_{-\infty}^{\infty} e^{-u^2} \phi(x + 2u \sqrt{t})\, du. \tag{4}$$

In order that this be a solution, it is necessary that ϕ be twice continuously differentiable and subject to some growth restriction (for example, of slow growth as $x \to \pm\infty$ in the sense of definition 17). Nevertheless, under much less restrictive conditions on ϕ the function defined by (4) will be infinitely differentiable, and will satisfy (1), for $t > 0$ and all x. Under such mild assumptions on ϕ, $z(x, t)$ will not in general be continuous for $t \geq 0$ and all x. The initial condition in the form (2) will not make sense and it will become necessary to interpret it in a generalized sense. The most familiar *generalized initial condition* is

$$z(x, t) \to \phi(x) \qquad \text{as} \qquad t \to 0, \tag{5}$$

to hold for each (or almost all) fixed x in I. Other generalized initial conditions involve convergence in norm,

$$\int_{-\infty}^{\infty} |z(x, t) - \phi(x)|^p\, dx \to 0 \qquad \text{as} \qquad t \to 0$$

where $p \geq 1$ is a fixed number; weak convergence,

$$\int_{-\infty}^{\infty} \psi(x)\, [z(x, t) - \phi(x)]\, dx \to 0 \qquad \text{as} \qquad t \to 0$$

for each integrable function ψ; or some other type of convergence.

The theory of existence and uniqueness of such generalized solutions encounters formidable difficulties which are briefly discussed in Carslaw and Jaeger (1947) section 12 where there are also references to the literature. In the case of an infinite or semi-infinite interval, these difficulties are illustrated by the function $Q(x, t)$ of section 5.3 which satisfies (1) for $t > 0$ and all x, vanishes when $x = 0$ and $t > 0$, and approaches zero for each fixed x as $t \to 0$; yet does not vanish identically. For the case of a finite interval the function $K(x, t)$ to be introduced in section 7.4 furnishes a similar example.

7.2 The Infinite Interval

We first investigate the diffusion equation in case I is the infinite interval $-\infty < x < \infty$. Equation 7.1(3) is a special case of equation 5.4(4), and we use the solution given by equation 5.4(5) with $w = \sqrt{s}$, $x_1 = -\infty$, $x_2 = \infty$, obtaining

$$z(x) = \frac{1}{2\sqrt{s}} \int_{-\infty}^{\infty} e^{-|x-y|\sqrt{s}} \phi(y)\, dy - \tfrac{1}{2} \int_{-\infty}^{\infty} R(x-y)\, \phi(y)\, dy$$

by equation 5.3(5). The tentative solution of the diffusion equation can thus be written as

$$z(x, t) = \tfrac{1}{2} \int_{-\infty}^{\infty} R(x-y, t)\, \phi(y)\, dy \qquad (1)$$

and, using the definition given by equation 5.3(1) of R and changing the variable of integration, this can be turned into equation 7.1(4).

THEOREM 26. Let $\phi(x)$ be locally integrable for all x and of slow growth as $x \to \pm \infty$. Then the function $z(x, t)$ defined by (1), or equation 7.1(4), is infinitely differentiable with respect to x and t, and satisfies the diffusion equation, when $t > 0$. Moreover, $z(x, 0+)$ exists and is equal to $\tfrac{1}{2}[\phi(x+) + \phi(x-)]$ for all those values of x for which $\phi(x+)$ and $\phi(x-)$ exist; in particular, equation 7.1(5) holds at all points of continuity of ϕ.

Proof. We have $(y-x)^2 \geq \tfrac{1}{2}y^2 - x^2$ for all real x and y and hence

$$R(x-y, t) = \frac{1}{\sqrt{\pi t}} \exp{-\frac{(x-y)^2}{4t}} \leq \frac{1}{\sqrt{\pi t}} \exp\left(-\frac{y^2}{8t} + \frac{x^2}{4t}\right).$$

If (x, t) is restricted to the rectangle $t_1 \leq t \leq t_2$, $-X \leq x \leq X$ where $t_1 > 0$, $X > 0$, we see that

$$0 < R(x-y, t) \leq \frac{1}{\sqrt{\pi t_1}} \exp\left(-\frac{y^2}{8t_2} + \frac{X^2}{4t_1}\right)$$

for all real y so that the convergence of the integral in (1) is dominated by the convergence of

$$\frac{1}{\sqrt{\pi t_1}} \exp\left(\frac{X^2}{4t_1}\right) \int_{-\infty}^{\infty} |\phi(y)| \exp\left(-\frac{y^2}{8t_2}\right) dy.$$

The last integral is convergent since ϕ is locally integrable and, according to definition 17, the integrand vanishes exponentially as $y \to \pm \infty$. Thus, the integral is uniformly convergent, and hence $z(x, t)$ is continuous, in every rectangle $0 < t_1 \leq t \leq t_2$, $-X \leq x \leq X$, and hence in the halfplane $t > 0$. Similar estimates for the partial derivatives of R show that the integrals obtained by differentiating (1) any number of times with respect to x and t under the integral sign are also uniformly convergent in each rectangle so that $z(x, t)$ is infinitely differentiable with respect to x and t for $t > 0$. Lastly, $R_{xx}(x - y, t) = R_t(x - y, t)$ by explicit computation, and hence $z(x, t)$ satisfies equation 7.1(1), for $t > 0$.

We have now established the theorem except for the statement about $z(x, 0+)$. Let x be fixed and such that $\phi(x+)$ exists. We wish to show that then

$$I = \int_{x}^{\infty} R(y - x, t) \, \phi(y) \, dy - \phi(x+) \to 0 \qquad \text{as} \qquad t \to 0. \qquad (2)$$

Now, by equation 5.3(1) and the substitution $y = x + 2u\sqrt{t}$,

$$\int_{x}^{\infty} R(y - x, t) \, dy = \frac{2}{\sqrt{\pi}} \int_{0}^{\infty} e^{-u^2} \, du = 1 \qquad (3)$$

so that

$$I = \int_{0}^{\infty} R(v, t) \, [\phi(x + v) - \phi(x+)] \, dv.$$

For any given $\epsilon > 0$ there exists a $\delta > 0$ so that $|\phi(x + v) - \phi(x+)| < \frac{1}{2}\epsilon$ when $0 < v < \delta$. Let us, then, write

$$I = \int_{0}^{\infty} = \int_{0}^{\delta} + \int_{\delta}^{\infty} = I_1 + I_2.$$

Clearly,

$$|I_1| = \left| \int_{0}^{\delta} R(v, t) \, [\phi(x + v) - \phi(x+)] \, dv \right| \leq \frac{1}{2}\epsilon \int_{0}^{\delta} R(v, t) < \frac{1}{2}\epsilon$$

by (3). Moreover, for $0 < t \leq 1$ and $v \geq \delta$,

$$R(v, t) = \frac{1}{\sqrt{\pi t}} \exp -\frac{v^2}{4t} \leq \frac{1}{\sqrt{\pi t}} \exp\left(-\frac{\delta^2}{4t}\right) \exp -\frac{v^2 - \delta^2}{4}$$

and hence

$$|I_2| = \left| \int_\delta^\infty R(v, t) \left[\phi(x + v) - \phi(x+) \right] dv \right|$$

$$\leq R(\delta, t) \int_\delta^\infty |\phi(x + v) - \phi(x+)| \exp \left(- \frac{v^2 - \delta^2}{4} \right) dv.$$

The last integral is convergent and is independent of t. Since $R(\delta, t) \to 0$ as $t \to 0$, we can choose t_0 so that $|I_2| < \frac{1}{2} \epsilon$ for $0 < t < t_0$. We then have $|I| < \epsilon$ for $0 < t < t_0$. Since ϵ was arbitrary, this proves (2). By a similar proof

$$\int_{-\infty}^x R(x - y, t) \, \phi(y) \, dy \quad \phi(x\ ) \quad > 0 \qquad \text{as} \qquad t \to 0$$

provided that $\phi(x\ )$ exists, and this completes the proof of theorem 26.

If $\phi(x)$ is twice continuously differentiable for all x and of slow growth as $x \to \perp \infty$, it can be shown that $z(x) = \{z(x, t)\}$ is in $C^2\mathfrak{C}$ and is an operator function of slow growth as $x \to \pm \infty$. It can then be deduced from theorem 20 that $z(x)$ is the unique solution of our problem. (See problem 1 for a special case of this.)

In the more general case envisaged in theorem 26 it can be proved, although we shall not do this here, that $z(x)$ is in $C^2\mathfrak{F}$ and is an operator function of slow growth, and theorem 20 can then be invoked to show that $z(x)$ is the unique solution of slow growth of equation 7.1(3) in $C^2\mathfrak{F}$. That this fact fails to give a significant uniqueness theorem for the diffusion equation is shown by the existence of solutions that fail to belong to $C^2\mathfrak{F}$ even though they are infinitely differentiable for all $t > 0$. Such a solution is $Q(x, t)$ for which we have from equation 5.3(1) and theorem 19, $Q(x) = e^{-x\sqrt{s}}$ when $x > 0$, $= 0$ when $x = 0$, $= - e^{x\sqrt{s}}$ when $x < 0$. Thus, the operator function $Q(x)$ is discontinuous at $x = 0$ even though $Q(x, t)$ is continuous for $t > 0$ and all x. [Note that $Q(x, t)$ is, however, discontinuous at $x = t = 0$.]

PROBLEMS

1. Let $\phi(x)$ be twice continuously differentiable for all x and assume that $\phi(x)$, $\phi'(x)$, $\phi''(x)$ are bounded. Prove that equation 7.1(4) represents a bounded solution of equation 7.1(1) for $t \geq 0$; and prove that this solution is unique in the class of solutions of slow growth of equation 7.1(1).

2. If $\phi(x) = 0$ for $x < 0$, $= 1$ for $x > 0$, express the solution $z(x, t)$ in terms of the error function. Discuss the behavior of this solution in the neighborhood of $x = 0$, $t = 0$.

3. Discuss the continuity and differentiability properties of the solution at and near $t = 0$ when $\phi(x) = 0$ for $x < 0$, $= x$ for $x > 0$.

7.3 The Semi-infinite Interval

We now turn to the semi-infinite interval $x \geq 0$ prescribing, in addition to the initial condition given by equation 7.1(5), the boundary condition

$$z(0+, t) = c(t). \tag{1}$$

We again use equation 5.4(5), this time with $w = \sqrt{s}$, $x_1 = 0$, $x_2 = \infty$, and take $a = 0$ in equation 5.4(6), this choice of a being suggested by theorem 20(ii). By calculations closely resembling those carried out in section 6.3 one obtains

$$z(x) = ce^{-x\sqrt{s}} + \frac{1}{2\sqrt{s}} \int_{-\infty}^{\infty} e^{-|x-y|\sqrt{s}} \operatorname{sgn} y \, \phi(|y|) \, dy = z_1(x) + z_2(x), \tag{2}$$

say. The second term, $z_2(x)$, is of the same same form as the solution obtained in the preceding section and can be transformed into a form analogous to equations 7.2(1) or 7.1(4), and in the first term, $z_1(x)$, we may use theorem 19. We then have

$$z_1(x, t) = \int_0^t Q(x, t - u) \, c(u) \, du \tag{3}$$

$$z_2(x, t) = \frac{1}{\sqrt{\pi}} \int_{-\infty}^{\infty} e^{-u^2} \operatorname{sgn}(x + 2u\sqrt{t}) \, \phi(|x + 2u\sqrt{t}|) \, du$$

$$z(x, t) = z_1(x, t) + z_2(x, t) \qquad\qquad x > 0, \, t > 0.$$

THEOREM 27. Let $\phi(x)$ be locally integrable for $x \geq 0$ and of slow growth as $x \to \infty$, and let $c \in \mathfrak{R}$. Then the function defined by (3) is infinitely differentiable with respect to x and t, and satisfies the diffusion equation, for $x > 0$, $t > 0$. Moreover, $z(x, 0+)$ exists and is equal to $\frac{1}{2}[\phi(x+) + \phi(x-)]$ for all those $x > 0$ for which $\phi(x+)$ and $\phi(x-)$ exist; and $z(0+, t)$ exists and is equal to $c(t-)$ for all those $t > 0$ for which $c(t-)$ exists.

Proof. $\phi(x)$ is defined for $x > 0$. If we extend this function to negative values of x by the definition $\phi(-x) = -\phi(x)$, then $z_2(x, t)$ becomes identical with the function defined in equation 7.1(4). By theorem 26, $z_2(x, t)$ is infinitely differentiable and satisfies equation 7.1(1) for $t > 0$ and all x, and $z_2(x, 0+) = \frac{1}{2}[\phi(x+) - \phi(x-)]$ in the sense stated in the theorem. Moreover $z_2(0+, t) = z_2(0, t)$ since $z_2(x, t)$ is continuous for all x if $t > 0$, and $z_2(0, t) = 0$ since the integrand is an odd function of u when $x = 0$. Thus, it remains to prove that $z_1(x, t)$ is an infinitely differentiable solution of equation 7.1(1) for $x > 0$, $t > 0$ satisfying the auxiliary conditions

$$z_1(0+, t) = c(t-), \qquad z_2(x, 0+) = 0.$$

It will be convenient to extend the definition of $Q(x, t)$ by setting $Q(x, t) = 0$ for $t \leq 0$. For $0 < t \leq T$ we may then write

$$z_1(x, t) = \int_0^T Q(x, t - u) \, c(u) \, du.$$

For $0 \leq u \leq T$, $0 < t \leq T$ and $x \geq \delta > 0$, $Q(x, t - u)$ is bounded, and possesses bounded derivatives of all orders with respect to x and t; and c is absolutely integrable over the interval $(0, T)$. It follows that z_1 is infinitely differentiable for $t \leq T$ and $x \geq \delta$, and since T and δ are arbitrary positive numbers, z_1 is infinitely differentiable for $t > 0$, $x > 0$. Since

$$Q_{xx}(x, t - u) = Q_t(x, t - u),$$

z_1 satisfies equation 7.1(1) when $x > 0$, $t > 0$.

Let us fix $x > 0$. We know from section 5.3 that $Q(x, t)$ is a monotonic increasing function of t when $t < \frac{1}{6} x^2$. Thus,

$$|z_1(x, t)| \leq |Q(x, t)| \int_0^t |c(u)| \, du \qquad 0 < t < \tfrac{1}{6} x^2,$$

and it follows that $z_1(x, 0+) = 0$ for each $x > 0$.

Now let us fix $t > 0$ and assume that $c(t-)$ exists. For any given $\epsilon > 0$ there is a $\delta > 0$ so that $|c(t-) - c(u)| < \frac{1}{3} \epsilon$ when $t - \delta < u < t$. By section 5.3, problem 3,

$$\int_0^t Q(x, t - u) \, du = \mathrm{Erfc} \frac{x}{2 \sqrt{t}},$$

and we write

$$z_1(x, t) - c(t-) = - \left(1 - \mathrm{Erfc} \frac{x}{2 \sqrt{t}} \right) c(t-)$$

$$+ \int_0^{t-\delta} Q(x, t - u) \, [c(u) - c(t-)] \, du$$

$$+ \int_{t-\delta}^t Q(x, t - u) \, [c(u) - c(t-)] \, du. \qquad (4)$$

Since $1 - \mathrm{Erfc}\, x/(2 \sqrt{t}) \to 0$ as $x \to 0$, there exists an $x_1 > 0$ so that the first term on the right-hand side of (4) is less than $\epsilon/3$ in absolute value whenever $0 < x < x_1$. If $x^2 < 6\delta$, then $Q(x, t - u)$ is a monotonic increasing function of u for $0 \leq u \leq t - \delta$ and in (4)

$$\left| \int_0^{t-\delta} \right| \leq Q(x, \delta) \int_0^{t-\delta} |c(u) - c(t-)| \, du.$$

$Q(x, \delta) \to 0$ as $x \to 0$, and there exists an $x_2 > 0$ so that $|\int_0^{t-\delta}| < \frac{1}{3} \epsilon$ when $0 < x < x_2$.

Lastly

$$\left| \int_{t-\delta}^{t} \right| < \frac{\epsilon}{3} \int_{0}^{t} Q(x, t - u) \, du = \frac{\epsilon}{3} \, \text{Erfc} \, \frac{x}{2 \sqrt{t}} < \frac{\epsilon}{3}.$$

Thus, $|z_1(x, t) - c(t-)| < \epsilon$ when $0 < x < \min(x_1, x_2)$, and the proof of theorem 27 is completed.

It can be proved that under the conditions of theorem 27 the operator function defined by (3) is of slow growth as $x \to \infty$ and is the only solution of slow growth of equations 7.1(3) and (1). As in the case of the infinite interval, and for similar reasons, this circumstance fails to provide an adequate basis for uniqueness theorems for generalized solutions of the diffusion equation.

PROBLEMS

1. Show that in order that $z(x, t)$ as given by (3) be twice continuously differentiable with respect to x, continuously differentiable with respect to t, and satisfy equation 7.1(1), for $x \geq 0$ and $t \geq 0$, it is necessary that $c(t)$ be continuously differentiable for $t \geq 0$, $\phi(x)$ be twice continuously differentiable for $x \geq 0$, and in addition that $c(0) = \phi(0)$, $c'(0) = \phi''(0)$.
If these conditions are satisfied, and $\phi(x)$, $\phi'(x)$, $\phi''(x)$ are bounded functions, show that $z(x, t)$ is bounded in each halfstrip $x \geq 0$, $0 \leq t \leq T$ and is unique in the class of solutions of slow growth of equation 7.1(1).

2. In (3) take $c(t) = t$ and $\phi(x) = x$ and investigate the continuity and differentiability of the solution near $x = t = 0$.

3. Solve equation 7.1(1) for $x > 0$, $t > 0$ given that $z(x, 0+) = 0$ for $x > 0$ and $z_x(0+, t) = c(t)$ for $t > 0$. Under suitable assumptions on c discuss this solution.

7.4 The Finite Interval

We conclude with the investigation of the diffusion equation on the closed interval I: $x_1 \leq x \leq x_2$ prescribing, in addition to the initial condition given by equation 7.1(5), the boundary conditions

$$z(x_1+, t) = c_1(t), \qquad z(x_2-, t) = c_2(t). \tag{1}$$

Then a computation similar to that described in section 6.4, except that it is based on $w = \sqrt{s}, f(x) = -\phi(x)$, leads to a unique solution of equation 7.1(3) in $C^2 \mathfrak{F}$.

Since the general formulas are involved we shall discuss only a special case.

EXAMPLE. To solve equation 7.1(1) for $0 < x < L$, $t > 0$ subject to the conditions

$$z(x, 0+) = z(0+, t) = 0, \qquad z(L-, t) = c(t-), \qquad (2)$$

where $0 < x < L$, $t > 0$, $c \in \mathfrak{R}$, and the last condition is supposed to hold wherever $c(t-)$ exists, in particular, at all points of continuity of c.

The appropriate solution of equation 7.1(3) with $\phi(x) = 0$ is obtained very much as the corresponding solution in 6.4, example 1, and is

$$z(x) = \frac{e^{x\sqrt{s}} - e^{-x\sqrt{s}}}{e^{L\sqrt{s}} - e^{-L\sqrt{s}}} . c. \qquad (3)$$

The analysis of this solution depends on the investigation of the Green's function of the problem,

$$K(x) = \{K(x, t)\} = \frac{e^{x\sqrt{s}} - e^{-x\sqrt{s}}}{e^{L\sqrt{s}} - e^{-L\sqrt{s}}} \qquad 0 \le x \le L. \qquad (4)$$

LEMMA 7. (i) $K(x, t) - Q(L - x, t)$ is infinitely differentiable for $0 \le x \le L$, $t \ge 0$. (ii) $K(x, t) - Q(L - x, t)$ vanishes along $t = 0$, $0 \le x \le L$ and along $x = L$, $t > 0$. (iii) $K(x, t)$ vanishes along $x = 0$, $t \ge 0$. Also

$$K(x, t) = \sum_{m=-\infty}^{\infty} Q(2mL + L - x, t) \qquad (5)$$

$$K(x, t) = \frac{2\pi}{L^2} \sum_{n=1}^{\infty} (-1)^{n-1} n e^{-n^2\pi^2 t/L^2} \sin\left(\frac{n\pi x}{L}\right). \qquad (6)$$

Proof. From (4),

$$K(x) = \frac{e^{-(L-x)\sqrt{s}} - e^{-(L+x)\sqrt{s}}}{1 - e^{-2L\sqrt{s}}}$$

$$= \sum_{m=0}^{\infty} e^{-(2mL+L-x)\sqrt{s}} - \sum_{m=0}^{\infty} e^{-(2mL+L+x)\sqrt{s}}$$

by section 4.2, example 1, and theorem 20(i). In the second sum we replace m by $-m-1$ and obtain

$$K(x) = \sum_{m=-\infty}^{\infty} \operatorname{sgn}(2mL + L - x) e^{-|2mL+L-x|\sqrt{s}}$$

This proves (5). The convergence of the expansion may be deduced from equation 5.3(2), the series on the right-hand side of (5) being dominated by

$$\sum_{m=-\infty}^{\infty} \frac{3\sqrt{6}}{(2mL + L - x)^2 \sqrt{\pi e^3}} = A.$$

Removing the term $m = 0$, it is seen that the expansion of $K(x, t) - Q(L - x, t)$ converges uniformly for $0 \leq x \leq L$, $t \geq 0$, and represents a continuous function. Similar estimates may be obtained for the derivatives, and (i) follows. To prove (ii), we remark that each term in the uniformly convergent expansion of $K(x, t) - Q(L - x, t)$ vanishes when $t = 0$, $0 \leq x \leq L$, and that the terms in this expansion cancel in pairs when $x = L$, $t \geq 0$. It follows that $K(x, t)$ itself vanishes for $t = 0$, $0 \leq x < L$ or $x = L$, $t > 0$, but $K(x, t)$ is discontinuous (and unbounded) at $x = L$, $t = 0$ (section 5.3). To prove (iii), we note that the expansion (5) converges uniformly when $0 \leq x \leq X < L$, $t \geq 0$, and the terms of (5) cancel in pairs when $x = 0$.

It follows from (5) that $K(x, t)$ is an odd periodic function of x, the period being $2L$. This function may be expanded in a Fourier series, and the coefficient of $\sin(n\pi x / L)$ in this Fourier series is

$$\alpha_n = \frac{1}{L} \int_{-L}^{L} K(x, t) \sin \frac{n\pi x}{L} \, dx.$$

Using

$$Q(2mL + L - x, t) = \frac{\partial}{\partial x} R(2mL + L - x, t),$$

integrating by parts, and interchanging summation and integration, we have

$$\alpha_n = - \sum_{m=-\infty}^{\infty} \frac{n\pi}{L^2} \int_{-L}^{L} R(2mL + L - x, t) \cos \frac{n\pi x}{L} \, dx.$$

Here we set $x = (2m + 1 + v) L$ to obtain

$$\alpha_n = \frac{(-1)^{n-1} n\pi}{L \sqrt{\pi t}} \int_{-\infty}^{\infty} \cos(n\pi v) \exp\left(-\frac{L^2 v^2}{4t}\right) dv$$

$$= \frac{2\pi n}{L^2} (-1)^{n-1} e^{-n^2 \pi^2 t / L^2},$$

and this proves (6). The expansion (6) converges uniformly, and may be differentiated any number of times, when $0 \leq x \leq L$, $t \geq t_0 > 0$.

We are now in the position to prove

THEOREM 28. If $c \in \mathfrak{K}$, the boundary value problem consisting of (2), and equation 7.1(1) has a unique solution $z(x) = \{z(x, t)\}$ such that $h^2 z(x) \in C^2 \mathfrak{C}$. This solution is given by

$$z(x, t) = \int_0^t K(x, t - u) c(u) \, du . \tag{7}$$

Proof. It can be shown that $z(x, t)$ is infinitely differentiable and satisfies equation 7.1(1) when $0 < x < L$, $t > 0$. From the series dominating the expansion (5), $|K(x, t)| \leq A$ for a fixed x, $0 < x < L$, so that

$$|z(x, t)| \leq A \int_0^t |c(u)|\, du,$$

and $z(x, 0+) = 0$ follows. If $0 \leq x < X < L$, $t \geq 0$, then $K(x, t)$ is continuous and we may make $x \to +0$ under the integral sign to prove $z(0+, t) = 0$ from lemma 7(iii). Lastly,

$$z(x, t) = \int_0^t Q(L - x, t - u)\, c(u)\, du + \int_0^t [K(x, t - u) - Q(L - x, t - u)]c(u)\, du.$$

The second term on the right-hand side vanishes as $x \to L$ by lemma 7(ii), and the first term approaches $c(t-)$ at every point at which $c(t-)$ exists by the proof of theorem 27. This proves $x(L-, t) = c(t-)$, and shows that (7) represents a solution of our boundary value problem.

PROBLEMS

1. Obtain the solution of the boundary value problem (1) in the form of a Fourier series. [Hint: use (6).]

2. Solve the diffusion equation 7.1(1) in the region $0 < x < L$, $t > 0$ given that

$$z(x, 0+) = 0 \qquad\qquad 0 < x < L$$

$$z_x(0+, t) = c(t), \qquad z(L-, t) = 0 \qquad\qquad t > 0.$$

References

Agnew, R. P., 1960: Differential equations, 2nd ed. McGraw-Hill.

Birkhoff, G. and S. MacLane, 1941: A survey of modern algebra. Macmillan.

Butzer, P. L., 1958: Die Anwendung des Operatorenkalküls von Jan Mikusiński auf lineare Integralgleichungen vom Faltungstypus. Arch. Rat. Mech. and Anal. 2, 114-128.

Butzer, P. L., 1959: Singular integral equations of Volterra type and the finite part of divergent integrals. Arch. Rat. Mech. and Anal. 3, 194-205.

Carslaw, H. S. and J. C. Jaeger, 1941: Operational methods in applied mathematics, Oxford University Press.

Carslaw, H. S. and J. C. Jaeger, 1947: Conduction of heat in solids. Oxford University Press.

Churchill, R. V., 1958: Operational mathematics, 2nd ed. McGraw-Hill.

Dalton, J. P., 1954: Symbolic operators. Witwatersrand University Press.

Doetsch, Gustav, H. Kniess, and Dietrich Voelker, 1947: Tabellen zur Laplace Transformation, Springer, Berlin and Göttingen.

Erdélyi, A., W. Magnus, F. Oberhettinger, and F. G. Tricomi, 1954: Tables of integral transforms, vol. I. McGraw-Hill.

Gardner, M. F. and J. L. Barnes, 1942: Transients in linear systems, I., John Wiley.

Halperin, I., 1952: Introduction to the theory of distributions. Based on lectures by Laurent Schwartz. University of Toronto Press.

Korevaar, J., 1955: Distributions defined from the point of view of applied mathematics. Proc. Kon. Ned. Ak. Wet. Amsterdam A 58, 368-389, 483-503, 663-674.

Lighthill, M. J., 1958: Introduction to Fourier analysis and generalized functions. Cambridge.

McLachlan, N. W., 1953: Complex variable theory and operational calculus, 2nd ed. Cambridge University Press.

Mikusiński, J. G., 1949, 1950: Sur le calcul opératoire, Časopis Pest. Mat. Fys. 74, 89-94.

Mikusiński, J. G., 1949: Sur les fondaments du calcul opératoire, Studia Math. 11, 41-70.

Mikusiński, J. G., 1950: Une nouvelle justification du calcul de Heaviside. Atti Accad. Naz. Lincei. Mem. Cl. Sci. Fis. Mat. Nat. (8) Ser. I, 2, 113-121.

Mikusiński, J. G., 1951: Sur les fonctions exponentielles du calcul opératoire. Studia Math. 12, 208-224.

Mikusiński, J. G., 1951: Sur les équations différentielles du calcul opératoire. et leurs applications aux équations classiques aux dérivées partielles. Studia Math. 12, 227-270.

Mikusiński, J. G., 1953: Rachunek operatorów, Warszawa.

Mikusiński, J. G., 1956: Le calcul opérationnel d'intervalle fini. Studia Math. 15, 225-251.

Mikusiński, J. G., 1959: Operational calculus. Pergamon Press.

Mikusiński, J. G. and C. Ryll-Nardzewski, 1951: Sur le produit de composition. Studia Math. 12, 51-57.

Mikusiński, J. G. and C. Ryll-Nardzewski, 1953: Un théorème sur le produit de composition des fonctions de plusieurs variables. Studia Math. 13, 62-68.

van der Pol, Balth., and H. Bremmer, 1950: Operational calculus, based on the two-sided Laplace integral. Cambridge University Press.

Sauer, R., 1958: Anfangswertprobleme bei partiellen Differentialgleichungen, 2nd. ed. Berlin.

Schmieden, C. and D. Laugwitz, 1958: Eine Erweiterung des Infinitesimalkalküls. Math. Zeits. 69, 1-39.

Schwartz, L., 1950, 1951: Théorie des distributions. 2 vols. Paris.

Temple, G., 1953: Theories and applications of generalized functions. J. London Math. Soc. 28 (1953) 134-148.

Titchmarsh, E. C., 1937: Introduction to the theory of Fourier integrals. Oxford University Press.

Weston, J. D., 1957: An extension of the Laplace-transform calculus. Rend. Circ. Mat. di Palermo (2) 6, 1-9.

Weston, J. D., 1959a: Operational calculus and generalized functions. Proc. Royal Soc. A 250, 460-471.

Weston, J. D., 1959b: Characterization of Laplace transforms and perfect operators. Arch. f. Rat. Mech. and Anal. 3, 348-354.

Widder, D. V., 1946: The Laplace Transform. Princeton University Press.

Answers to Problems

Section 1.3

2. $\int_{-\infty}^{\infty} \delta^{(n)}(u) f(t-u) \, du = f^{(n)}(t)$

Section 2.1

1. Nos. 1, 2, 4, 6, $\{(t+1)^{-1}\}$, $\{(t+1)^{\pm 1/2}\}$, $\{|t-1|^{1/2}\}$, $\{(t+\alpha)^{-1}\}$ except when α is zero or negative, $\{\exp(t-1/t)\}$ provided the function is defined to be zero at $t=0$, nos. 12, 15, 16. **3.** (i) $\{t^{n-1} e^t/n!\}$; (ii) $\{\Gamma(\alpha+1)\,\Gamma(\beta+1)t^{\alpha+\beta+1}/\Gamma(\alpha+\beta+2)\}$; (iii) $\{[\Gamma(\alpha+1)]^n \, t^{n\alpha+n-1}/\Gamma(n\alpha+n)\}$ **4.** (i) $\{t\}$; (ii) $-4 \{\sinh t - t\}$

Section 2.4

2. Those that belong to $\mathfrak{C}$, and $\{|t-1|^{-1/2}\}$. **3.** $h^{\beta+1}/h^{\beta} = h = \{1\}$, $h^{\alpha}/h^{\beta} = h^{\alpha-\beta} = \{t^{\alpha-\beta-1}\}/\Gamma(\alpha-\beta)$ if $\operatorname{Re}\alpha > \operatorname{Re}\beta$. **4.** $h^{\alpha}/h^{\alpha} = 1$ is the unit operator ("delta function"), $h^{\beta-1}/h^{\beta} = h^{-1}$ (see end of section). **5.** Choose a positive integer n so that $n + \operatorname{Re}(\alpha-\beta) > 1$. Then $h^n f = h^{n+\alpha-\beta} = \{t^{n+\alpha-\beta-1}/\Gamma(n+\alpha-\beta)\}$. Differentiate n times. **7.** The subset is that of continuous functions vanishing at $t=0$ and possessing a locally integrable derivative. **8.** $h(\alpha f + \beta g) = \alpha\, hf + \beta\, hg$; $hf\, hg = h^2 fg \neq hfg$ (unless $f = \{0\}$ or $g = \{0\}$).

Section 3.1

1. See section 2.4, problem 5. **2.** $g^{(n)} = h^{\alpha-n}f$. For $f \in \mathfrak{R}$, $h^{\alpha}f$ is n times continuously differentiable if $\operatorname{Re}\alpha > n$, and possesses a locally integrable derivative of order n if $\alpha = n$; the other results remain unchanged. **3.** $f = h^n f^{(n)}$, $s^{\alpha}f = h^{n-\alpha}f^{(n)}$. **4.** (i) $\alpha s + (\beta - \alpha\omega^2)\{\cos \omega t\}$; (ii) $\alpha + \beta s$ **5.** The finite part is equal to $\Gamma(-\alpha)s^{\alpha}f$ if $f(0) = f'(0) = \cdots = f^{(n-1)}(0) = 0$. In the general case, use $s^{\alpha}f = s^{\alpha-n}[f^{(n)} + \sum_{k=1}^{n} h^{k-n}f^{(k-1)}(0)]$ and problem 1. **6.** The two are equal. **8.** (i) $\{\phi''(x+t) + \phi''(|x-t|)\,\operatorname{sgn}(x-t)\} + 2s\phi(x) - 2\phi(0)\,h_{-1}(x)$; (ii) $\{\phi'(x-t) - \phi'(|x-t|)\} + 2\phi(x) - 2\phi(0)\,h_0(x)$ **9.** $s^2 f = f'' + f'(0) + f(0)s + [f'(x+) - f'(x-)]\,h_0(x) + [f(x+) - f(x-)]\,h_{-1}(x)$

Section 3.2

2. (i) $\{t^{n-1}e^{-\alpha t}/(n-1)!\}$, (ii) $\{\lambda e^{-\alpha t} \cosh \beta t + (\mu - \alpha\lambda)\beta^{-1}e^{-\alpha t} \sinh \beta t\}$, (iii) $\{\lambda \cos \alpha t + \dfrac{\rho + \alpha^2\mu}{2\alpha^3} \sin \alpha t + \dfrac{\nu - \alpha^2\lambda}{2\alpha} t \sin \alpha t - \dfrac{\rho - \alpha^2\mu}{2\alpha^2} t \cos \alpha t\}$ **3.** $\alpha(\alpha a^2 + \beta)/[(s-1)(s^2+\omega^2)]$

Section 3.3

1. $(\alpha^{-1} + 2\alpha)e^{-t} \sin \alpha t + \cos \alpha t - 2\alpha \sin \alpha t$ **2.** $(t-1)^2 e^{-t}$ **3.** $e^{-t} + \frac{1}{2}(t^3 - 3t^2 + 3t - 1)e^t$ **4.** $x = \alpha \left\{ \frac{4}{51} e^{-t/4} + \frac{5}{87} e^{-2t/5} - \frac{67}{493} \cos t + \frac{21}{493} \sin t \right\}$‘ $y = \alpha \left\{ \frac{4}{51} e^{-t/4} - \frac{10}{87} e^{-2t/5} - \frac{18}{493} \cos t + \frac{13}{493} \sin t \right\}$ **5.** $x(t) = 2e^{2t} - 2 \cos t - 3t \sin t$, $y(t) = \sin t + t \cos t - 2t \sin t$ **6.** $\sin \alpha t/(\alpha \cos \alpha T)$ if $\cos \alpha T \neq 0$. No solution if $\cos \alpha T = 0$. **7.** No solution if $\omega T = (2n+1)\pi$, an infinity of solutions if $\omega T = 2n\pi$, unique solution if $\omega T \neq n\pi$ (n integer). **8.** $x(t) = -\frac{1}{3}(\cos t + \cos 2t)$, $y(t) = -\frac{1}{3}(\sin t - \sin 2t)$

Section 3.4

1. $\left\{ e^{t^2} + 2 \int_0^t (t-u-1)e^{u-t+u^2} \, du \right\}$ **2.** $\{e^t\}$ or $1 - \{e^t\}$ **3.** $\{\alpha \cos \sqrt{\omega^2 - \beta\omega} \, t\}$ **4.** $\{\alpha \cos [\omega t(1-\beta)^{-1/2}]\}$ if $\beta \neq 1$, no solution if $\beta = 1$ **5.** $\left\{ \alpha \int_0^t [nu^{n-1} + \beta \sqrt{\pi} \, n! \, u^{n-1/2}/\Gamma(n+\frac{1}{2})] \, e^{\pi\beta^2(t-u)} \, du \right\}$ if $n = 1, 2, 3, \cdots$; $\left\{ ae^{\pi\beta^2 u} + a\beta \int_0^t u^{1/2} e^{-\pi\beta^2(t-u)} \, du \right\}$ if $n = 0$. **6.** $0 < \alpha < 1$, ϕ continuous and possesses a locally integrable derivative.

Section 4.1

1. No. **3.** $|\alpha_n|^{1/n} \to 0$ as $n \to \infty$ **4.** Use Schwarz's inequality for f^2, estimate f^3 from $f^2 f$, and prove the general result by induction. **7.** $h^2 a_n = \{t - 1/n\} \to h^2$ uniformly. $a_n^{-1} = -n/(s-n) = \{-ne^{nt}\}$. If $p a_n^{-1}$ converges uniformly for some $p \in \mathfrak{C}$, then $n \int_0^t e^{nu} p(t-u) \, du$ is bounded, for fixed t, as $n \to \infty$, and $p = 0$ by section 2.2, lemma 2.

Section 4.2

1. (i) not convergent. Proof as in section 4.1, problem 7, or from (ii) by means of $(n \mid \alpha s)^{-1} = n^{-1} - \alpha s/[n(n+\alpha s)]$. (ii) $h \sum [n(n+\alpha s)]^{-1} = \sum \{n^{-2}(1 - e^{-nt/\alpha})\}$, uniform convergence by comparison with $\sum n^{-2}$. (iii) convergent. **3.** If $p \in \mathfrak{C}$ and $p a_n$, $n = 1, 2, \cdots$, is a uniformly convergent sequence of continuous functions, then $|p a_n(t)|$, $0 \leq t \leq T$, $n = 1, 2, \cdots$ is bounded for each fixed $T > 0$. **4.** Convergence from theorem 10(i). Use equation 4.1(4) with $\alpha = 0$ to justify formal operations with series. **5.** For $\nu \neq 0, 1, 2, \cdots$ use $\binom{\nu}{n} = (-1)^n n^{-\nu-1}[1 + O(n^{-1})]/\Gamma(-\nu)$ as $n \to \infty$ to prove convergence of the series in cases (i), (ii). **6.** (i) $f \in \mathfrak{R}_\alpha$ in this case. (ii) Use equation 4.1(4) with $\alpha = 0$. $A \sum M^n n^{-n\delta}$ is convergent. (iii) Use equation 4.1(4) and Stirling's formula. $A \sum M^n n^{-n\delta}/\Gamma(n\alpha + 1)$ is convergent. **7.** See Mikusiński (1959) p. 166 f.

Section 4.3

1. $2h^2/(x^2 s^2 + 2) = \{t - (x/\sqrt{2}) \sin (\sqrt{2} \, x^{-1} t)\}$. Both operator functions are continuous for all x. **2.** (ii) $h\{\phi(x+t) + \phi(x-t)\} = \{\int_{x-t}^{x+t} \phi(y) \, dy\}$ **3.** The integral is a bounded continuous function of $t \geq 0$ and all x. **4.** Yes, for all x. **5.** Take β so that $\mathrm{Re}\,(\alpha + \beta) > 1$. Then $h^\beta h_\alpha(x)$ is a continuous function of x

and t which vanishes when $x > t$. **6.** $[h_0(x)]^n = h_0(nx) \to 0$ as $n \to \infty$. **7.** (i) convergent for all $c_n \, \epsilon \, \mathfrak{C}$. (ii) Convergent if there exists a $p \neq 0$ such that $pc_n \, \epsilon \, \mathfrak{C}$ for all n. **8.** See theorem 18(i). **9.** See theorem 18, corollary.

Section 4.4

1. $- s^3/x^2 \left\{ te^{-t/x} \right\}$, $- s^4/(x^2 \sqrt{2}) \left\{ t \sin (t \sqrt{2})/x \right\}$ **2.** If pa, $pb \, \epsilon \, C$, then $pa\phi(x)$ and $pb\psi(x)$ are continuously differentiable with respect to x. **3.** Set $h^2 f(x) = F(x)$. Then $F(x, t) = \int_x^{x+t} (t + x - y) \, \phi(y) \, dy + \int_{x-t}^x (t - x + y) \, \phi(y) \, dy$ and $\partial^2 F / \partial x^2 = \phi(x + t) + \phi(x - t) - 2\phi(x)$ by explicit computation. The result cannot be extended to sectionally continuous functions. $g(x) = hf(x) \, \epsilon \, C^2$ if and only if $\phi(x)$ is continuous. **4.** Set $\phi_1(x) = \text{sgn } x \, \phi(|x|)$ and use problem 3.

Section 4.5

4. The integrals are twice continuously differentiable, and $a = b = 0$ by section 4.3, problem 9.

Section 5.1

1. $[z(x)]^{-1} = [z(0)]^{-2} \, z(- x)$. **2.** $V(x) = Z(x) \, z(x_0 - x)$ satisfies $V'(x) = f(x) \, z(x_0 - x)$ and $V(x_0) = z_0$.

Section 5.2

1. Use example 1. **2.** See Mikusiński (1959) p. 400 f.

Section 5.3

1. $s^{-3}(e^{-xs} - e^{-ys}) = \left\{ 0 \text{ if } 0 \leq t \leq x, \ \frac{1}{2}(t - x)^2 \text{ if } x \leq t \leq y, \ \frac{1}{2}(y - x) \right.$ $\times (2t - x - y)$ if $t \geq x \}$. **2.** Use section 4.3, problem 6. **3.** Use problem 2. **4.** Use problem 3. **5.** See Mikusinski (1959) p. 195 f. **6.** Use problem 2. **7.** $- |y| \leq x \leq |y|$. $\sinh xs/(s \cosh ys) = s^{-1}[e^{-(y-x)s} - e^{-(y+x)s}]/(1 - e^{-2ys})$. Use problems 1 and 3, and expand in a Fourier series. **8.** For the second part, apply s and h to (5). **9.** Similar to theorem 19: use $(s + \alpha)^{-1}$ in place of h. **10.** Yes. **11.** For $\epsilon > 0$, there exists an $x_0(\epsilon)$ such that for every $x > x_0(\epsilon)$, $|x^{-2} \log |\phi(x)|| < \epsilon/2$ and $|\phi(x)| < \exp \frac{1}{2} \epsilon x^2$. **13.** Use theorem 20(i).

Section 5.4

2. Apply section 4.5, problem 1, to (6) with $f(x) = s\phi(x)$. **3.** Use theorems 22 and 20.

Section 5.5

1. $e^t(1 - e^{-\omega[t/\omega]}) (1 - e^{-\omega})^{-1}$ **2.** $\sum_{n=0}^{[t/\omega]} (n + 1) f(t - n\omega)$ **3.** $3^{k+2} - 2^{k+2}$ **5.** $z_1(t) = \sum_{n=0}^{[t/2]} f(t - 2n) + \sum_{n=0}^{[(t-1)/2]} g(t - 2n - 1)$

Section 6.1

1. $z_{xx} + \alpha z_x - s^2 c^{-2} z = - c^{-2} z_t(x, 0) - sc^{-2} z(x, 0)$ **2.** $z(x, t) = 0$ if $0 \leq t \leq x^2/2$, $= (t - x^2/2)^2$ if $t \geq x^2/2$.

Section 6.2

2. $z_{xx} = z_{tt} = \frac{1}{2} \delta(x + t) + \frac{1}{2} \delta(x - t)$ **3.** $z(x, t) = 0$ if $0 \leq t \leq x^2/2$, $= t - x^2/2$ if $t \geq x^2/2$ is a generalized solution (derivatives fail to exist when $t = x^2/2 > 0$).

Section 6.3

3. (i) ϕ twice continuously differentiable, ψ, v continuously differentiable, $v(0) = \phi'(0)$, $v'(0) = \psi'(0)$.

Section 6.4

1. $s^2 c \in \mathfrak{C}_0$ **2.** Yes. **4.** ϕ twice continuously differentiable, $\phi(0) = \phi''(0) = \phi(L) - \phi''(L) = 0$. **5.** $gh^2[(e^{-s(L-x)/c} + e^{sx/c})(1 + e^{-sL/c})^{-1} - 1]$

Section 7.2

2. $\frac{1}{2}$ Erfc $[- x/(2 \sqrt{t})]$. Discontinuous at $x = t = 0$. **3.** Continuous for $t \geq 0$ and all x, not differentiable at $x = t = 0$.

Section 7.3

2. Continuous. Partial derivatives of order one exist.

3. $z(x, t) = - \dfrac{1}{\sqrt{\pi}} \displaystyle\int_0^t c(t - u) \exp\left(- \dfrac{x^2}{4u}\right) \dfrac{du}{\sqrt{u}}$

Notations

The references are to sections.

$\mathfrak{C}$	2.1, definition 1.
C, $C\mathfrak{C}$, $C\mathfrak{F}$, $C\mathfrak{R}$, $C(I)$, etc.	4.3, definition 12.
C^n	4.4, definition 13.
e^{xw}	5.2.

$$\text{Erfc } z = \frac{2}{\sqrt{\pi}} \int_z^\infty e^{-v^2}\, dv$$

ϵ is contained in, is a member of

$\mathfrak{F}$	2.3, definition 4.
h, h^α	2.1.
$h_\alpha(x)$, $h_\alpha(x, t)$	4.3, example 3.

$$H(t) = \begin{array}{ll} 0 & \text{if} \quad t < 0 \\ 1 & \text{if} \quad t \geq 0 \end{array}$$

$I_0(xs)$	5.4, problem 5.

$$J_n(z) = \sum_{k=0}^\infty \frac{(-1)^k\, (z/2)^{n+2k}}{k!\, \Gamma(k+n+1)}.$$

$\mathfrak{K}$	2.4, definition 5.
$K_0(xs)$	5.4, problem 5.
$\mathfrak{N}$	2.1, definition 1.
O	4.1.
$Q(x)$, $Q(x, t)$	5.3.
$R(x)$, $R(x, t)$	5.3.
s, s^α	3.1.

$$\text{sgn } x = \begin{array}{ll} 1 & \text{if} \quad x > 0. \\ 0 & \text{if} \quad x = 0. \\ -1 & \text{if} \quad x < 0. \end{array}$$

$[x]$ largest integer $\leq x$.

$\{f(t)\}$	1.6.
$f(x+)$, $f(x-)$	3.1, problem 9.

$$ab(t) = \int_0^t a(u)\, b(t-u)\, du.$$

a/b	2.3, definition 3.

Subject Index

Absolutely integrable, 10
Algebra, 22

Continuity of operator functions, 8
Convergence
    of convolution quotients, 8, 43f
    uniform, 43
Convolution, 8, 14f, 24, 27
Convolution quotients, 1, 2, 8f
Convolution ring, 14f

Derivative
    extended, 29, 33
    locally integrable, 10, 28f, 35
    of operator function, 54f
Difference equations, 70f
Differential equation, 35f, 59f
Diffusion equation, 85f
Distributions, 7f
Divisor of zero, 16f

Embedding, 23f

Field of convolution quotients, 20f
Function
    Bessel, 40f, 50, 61, 66
    delta, 1, 4f, 8, 25, 33, 45, 47, 61
    error, 66f, 89, 91
    exponential, 2, 60f
    generalized, 1, 6f, 25f
    generating, 70
    Heaviside's unit, 5, 9, 14, 29, 53
    impulse, 1, 5, 6, 8, 33
    locally integrable, 9f, 23f, 27
    numerical, 52
    operator, 2, 8, 51f
    of slow growth, 64f, 67, 87, 89f, 92

Heaviside calculus, 1f

Integral
    finite part of, 31f
    of fractional order, 15
    of operator function, 56f
Integral equations, 39f, 49
Integration, 9f

Laplace transformation, 3f, 34, 37
Lerch's theorem, 18
Logarithm, 60f

Operational calculus, 1f
Operator, 1, 26
    of differentiation, 8, 23, 26, 28f
    of integration, 8, 9, 23, 26
    numerical, 25
    perfect, 26
    shift, 53

Power series, 48f

Recurrence relation, 70, 72f

Sequence, of convolution quotients, 43f
Series, of convolution quotients, 48f
Singularity, of a locally integrable function,
    9f
Solution, generalized, 76f, 80, 84, 86f
Symbolic method, 2

Telegraphist's equation, 76

Value, of a generalized function, 25f
Vector space, 15, 22, 24, 27

Wave equation, 75f